REVIEWS

"I love Dr. Rosenthal's materials. I have been in recovery for 20 years and teaching groups ... 18. This is the best teaching tool I have ever used. My clients and I are grateful." – Renita Kitchingham, MAADCII

"Once again, Rosenthal has knocked it out of the park. I absolutely love her work. I use it all the time, and my clients are very receptive. It's truly a breath of fresh air. I adore her approach with humor and pictures, and the information is very thorough. She asks questions to get clients thinking about their lives and choices. I especially love the breaks, puzzles, and mind games and how Rosenthal incorporates recovery into them. I will definitely use this in my curriculum. Thank you for doing what you do. It is amazing!!!" – Charlotte Prather, SUDC

"I run an outpatient group that ranges from emerging adults to Silver Sneakers, and it doesn't matter the age group: When they see an OTB-Recovery Workbook, they know they're going to learn something cool! I have a dual diagnosis group, and even those without primary substance abuse disorders learn something every time we use a lesson from OTB. Recovery from any disorder is tough work, and the whimsical artwork and intriguing lessons add some levity to difficult subject matter. The funny/quirky way Rosenthal approaches lessons really resonates with my clients." – Mike Dalton, MA, LAC

"The thing I love the most about the workbook is how easy it was to follow and engage in the activities. My favorite was writing a poem about addiction, then adding a happy ending (the hope of recovery). This is absolutely something clinicians and recovery coaches can utilize with their clients/participants." – Tanya Wessells, CRSW

"I stumbled on Dr. Rosenthal's website a couple of years ago. The therapists in our group looooovvee the handouts and use them with regularity. The owner of the company loved it so much that she purchased a book for each of the offices under her tutelage. We are looking forward to the next book. Thank you so much for all that you do!!!" – Sheri Cannon, LPN

"I discovered the OTB Recovery worksheets last year, and I have been using them with patients. The quizzes work well as an icebreaker and starting point in groups, and I have found the humor particularly helpful for my young adult clients to start exploring the possibility of recovery." – Mandy Stokes, MSW, SACSSP

"I am new to facilitating groups, but I find this workbook is a great starting place. I'm beginning to incorporate it more and more into my group work. My boss is just amazed with all the information and fun things that Rosenthal has put together. " – Michele Hunter, BA, DIC

"I like the content of the material, down-to-earth practical information that's easy to understand for clients of all ages." – Brenda A. Cleary, LCDC

"I absolutely love OTB! I have handed out worksheets as individual assignments for someone to work on if they are struggling in a certain area. They grab my clients' interest immediately and their laughter breaks down walls. I've recommended OTB to several of my peers." – Karin Kaufmann, ARS, ACIT, CAPRC-II

"I absolutely love the creativity and thought that Dr. Kim put into this workbook. Not only has it helped me bring my group therapy sessions to life, it has also been a game changer for my recovery. There are so many ice-breaker questions and activities that my clients enjoy. If you're on the fence about getting this workbook, I suggest DO IT! It gets clients engaged, and they say they feel like they aren't walking away empty-handed. The best thing about the OTB-Recovery Workbook is that it's not just 'do the worksheet and be done.' It's a 'Do the work, learn, and use the skills' type of thing! People in recovery need to learn the skills taught in this workbook in order to continue to work on themselves daily. And the best feeling you can have as a group therapy leader is when the clients say, 'I can't wait until next week.' Thanks, Dr. Kim, for all the hard work you put into this workbook." – Serena Smith, CRSS

"The workbook is really good and has been helpful with clients. It is presented in a way that is not boring or overbearing. I have never had a negative response. Clients always laugh, and we can have a relaxed conversation. Some clients enjoy the coloring, and I use that interest to teach how easy it can be to get your mind busy. In 7-10 minutes, the craving will pass." – Roger Dodd, Peer Support Worker

"I work in inpatient rehab, and the ladies love the exercises in Rosenthal's first book. I can't wait to use this next great book in my practice." – Wendi Percha, SUD Counselor

"I love the concept of this book. I'm able to photocopy worksheet pages for my clients then provide them with coloring pencils to use in conjunction with the work in the handout. This is a great and valuable resource!" – Lisa Ackland, LLMSW, DP-CAADC

"I'm an addiction counselor and planned on using the book with my clients. Well, they loved it! They were excited to have something different. By observation, it came to my attention that my clients tend to be more truthful when they are having fun with it. I want to thank Dr. Rosenthal for the great research, focus, and true compassion that she has for mental health. Thank you for everything you do!" – Julie Wright, CAC-AD

"I thoroughly enjoyed this book and all it has to offer. I am a licensed counselor and work primarily with substance abuse clients, and this book offers great worksheets not only for individual sessions but also for groups. I like that it implements different activities such as drawing and writing. I think this is a great addition to any counselor's library." – Bobby Jo Appleton, MS, LAC

The Second Outside-the-Box Recovery Workbook

Kim Rosenthal, MD

RELAPSE PREVENTION • MINDFULNESS • NARRATIVE THERAPY
MOTIVATIONAL INTERVIEWING • ART/EXPRESSIVE THERAPY
COGNITIVE BEHAVIORAL THERAPY • SKILL-BUILDING • MATRIX MODEL

©2022 Kim Rosenthal, MD
The SECOND Outside-the-Box Recovery Workbook:
Illustrated, Fun, and Professional Handouts for Drug Counselors and Their Clients

Kim Rosenthal, MD
Rosenthal Publishing, LLC
P.O Box 2783
Lenoir, NC 28645
kimrosenthalmd.com

The information in this publication is not intended to be a substitution for consultation with a health care professional. Individual health concerns should be assessed by a qualified clinician.

Care has been taken to confirm the accuracy of the information presented. However, the author is not responsible for errors or any consequences derived from the application of this information, and she makes no warranty, expressed or implied, for the contents in this book.

All names and events described in this workbook are fictional. Any likeness to real people is coincidental.

Author and illustrator: Kim Rosenthal, MD
Cover artist: Kim Rosenthal, MD
Biography photographer: Ed Laws

First Edition printed July 2022.

Rosenthal, Kim (2022). *The SECOND Outside-the-Box Recovery Workbook: Illustrated, Fun, and Professional Handouts for Drug Counselors and Their Clients.* Lenoir, NC: Rosenthal Publishing, LLC

ISBN 978-1-7369741-2-4

Printed in the United States.

To my Angelín, who understood why I spent the last year in my writing-closet. Thanks for climbing in and keeping me company!

To my friend and photographer and IT god, Eduardo, who laughed at my jokes, took great pics, and kept my laptop in good humor.

To my editors, reviewers, readers, family, friends, and you! Thanks for your support. I owe you a great big virtual box of chocolates!

I hope you feel beautiful today. – Anonymous

AN INTRODUCTION FOR COUNSELORS

I WAS ON-CALL AT THE HOSPITAL when I was asked to see a young girl with a heroin addiction. The 13-year-old had used a dirty needle that caused a blood infection. Her heart reacted by swelling to an enormous size, and soon it wasn't strong enough to support her body. So, there the teen sat on the hospital bed, skin pale, oxygen tubing over her face, her hands a coarse tremor. She was dying, and she was in a panic. I tried to calm the child, but what could I say? *Everything will be okay? Focus on the moment?* It was too late: The following morning the room was empty. One life over.

Drugs kill. Every year, more than 11.4 million people die worldwide from drugs and alcohol. That's one death every 3 seconds!* How many have died since you started reading this page? It's staggering. These numbers aren't just statistics. They're horrible diseases, devastated families, lost dreams, and completely avoidable deaths. The relapse and death rate are extremely high in addiction, which underscores the need to find new ways to approach substance use treatment.

Why is quitting drugs so difficult? Abstinence takes enormous effort, but people who seek recovery aren't always welcomed with open arms. Consequences float around like black clouds. Problems crop up. Emotions run crazy. Coping skills are mysterious concepts. Families are hurt and hypercritical. Boredom is the game of the day. Joy is hard to find, and when frustration or anger is your friend, sobriety lacks a quick "get relief now" button. By the time people reach our clinic doors, they come with one major question: *Is recovery worth it?* There's the issue: Recovery can be playful, fulfilling, and amazing, but how do we help clients understand that when their lives are in shambles? We need treatment material that appeals to this population, something to keep them in treatment and remind them recovery is rewarding!

Awash with illustrations, cartoons, and a pinch of the comical, *The SECOND Outside-the-Box Recovery Workbook* fills a growing need for evidence-based manuals that embrace creativity and fun. Why creativity and fun? The answer is simple: Creativity helps clients process difficult issues in a safe way; it makes room for conversation and change. Fun brings joy to often turbulent lives. In fact, studies show that combining creativity and fun with mainstream treatment reduces relapse rate and promotes treatment retention.

We're talking about evidence-based creativity and fun, like art therapy, expressive writing, narrative therapy, mindful coloring, and humor therapy. These treatment modalities don't replace traditional interventions. They augment them. In this workbook, you'll find the Matrix Model, relapse prevention, cognitive behavioral therapy, interpersonal skills, assertive communication, and other modalities. You'll also find poetry, drawing, coloring, and playwriting. It all counts.

What's the take-home message? *The SECOND Outside-the-Box Recovery Workbook* walks alongside providers and clients during the difficult moments, offering a unique, friendly, and creative approach to challenging tasks. Together, we figure out how to survive the devastation of addiction. We laugh a bit and seek joy too. There's room for play, even silliness. Recovery isn't always filled with humor, but we need it, don't we? Despite the tragedies, there's hope. Over time, clients finds great joy in who they are, what they surround themselves with, and a future filled with potential. This workbook stays with your client and you as they embark on this journey.

Kim Rosenthal, MD
kimrosenthalmd.com

[*] https://ourworldindata.org/drug-use. Our World in Data: Drug Use (2019)

WELCOME TO RECOVERY

TABLE OF CONTENTS

WELCOME

You've reached *The SECOND Outside-the-Box Recovery Workbook.* Here we take you on a fresh journey into the world of sobriety, where hard work meets illustrations, poetry, artwork, cartoons, puzzles, maps, odd situations, and a bit of humor. With this book as a guide, you'll learn more about:

- Dealing with cravings and triggers
- Understanding your feelings
- Using mindfulness, gratitude, and journaling to calm tough emotions
- Recognizing problem thoughts and improving them
- Creating a schedule and replacing bad stuff with good
- Practicing honesty, assertiveness, and being a better friend
- Handling tough relationships
- Remembering your self-worth

Whether you're a seasoned provider using this workbook with clients or someone new to sobriety, join us for another trek into this colorful land called Outside-the-Box Recovery!

INSTRUCTIONS

1. Please find yourself a copy of this workbook, then grab a pen or pencil and complete all tasks in writing (or drawing, coloring, puzzling, rapping, flower-pressing, etc).

2. Share all your work with someone wise: sponsor, mentor, counselor, shrink… a person who understands recovery.

3. Take a deep breath and go to the next page.

HOW TO USE THIS BOOK

Please Read and Sign

I will show up for recovery and do the work. When I don't do the work, I'll pick myself up and go back to doing the work.

I promise to write all answers and do all exercises to the best of my ability.

I will not give up. Period.

I will laugh at anything that's remotely funny.

I will complete this book under the guidance of someone wise.

I will reach out for help if I need it.

Signed _____

Date _____

MORE STUFF

Here's the small print.

ANSWERS. See appendix A (page 135) for answers to all brainteasers and puzzles.

TAKE A BREAK. There are nine "Take A Break" pages. They're just spots to kick back a moment before going onto the next worksheet.

CLINICIANS. If you're a mental health professional, please see Appendix B (page 159) for general background and specific recommendations for each worksheet. Also, see pages 127-132 for extra handouts.

VOCAB. The words "substance use disorder," "substance use," "substance dependence," "Chemical dependency," "addiction," "using," "drug problem," "alcohol problem," and other variations of the concept don't mean the same thing. However, we've used them interchangeably throughout this book to avoid repeating the same word over and over. No offense is meant to anyone!

MORE VOCAB. We've also used the words "clean," "sober," and "abstinent" in the same way.

RECOVERY
PLAN 101

RECOVERY PLAN

5

PURPOSE OF THIS HANDOUT

- To prepare for recovery
- To do even *more* preparation!

WE WISH IT WERE AS SIMPLE AS, "I QUIT. YEAH, IT'S OVER!" It isn't. Sobr
more than just quitting. It's about creating the new YOU in recovery, but that comes w.
Welcome to your Early Recovery Plan. Please answer all questions.

1. Why quit? List three reasons you choose recovery.

_____

_____

_____

_____

2. Where to start? Check the options that helped or might help you quit.

- ☐ Go to an emergency room for help
- ☐ Detox from drugs/alcohol
- ☐ Call SAMHSA national substance abuse hotline at 800-662-HELP for guidance
- ☐ Contact my family doctor for a referral
- ☐ Call my health insurance for a referral
- ☐ Participate in an inpatient rehab
- ☐ Participate in a residential rehab
- ☐ Find a sober living house
- ☐ Go to an intensive outpatient program
- ☐ See a counselor or psychiatrist
- ☐ Attend 12-Step meetings
- ☐ Attend a support group
- ☐ Quit alone (please don't check this one)
- ☐ Treatments that have helped in the past:

_____

_____

_____

_____

3. Who to tell? Who knows that you've qu
Name two people who care and will hold you
to your word. Include phone numbers. If you
haven't yet, let them know now.

_____

_____

_____

_____

4. Associated goal? Which is your biggest goal right now? (Check all that apply.)

- ☐ To stay clean
- ☐ ~~To save up for a yacht~~
- ☐ To stay clean

6 ...covery takes change! Check ...'ve made since quitting, then ...ones you haven't begun yet.

5. H...
...g drugs/alcohol
...octor for a physical exam
...d of drug paraphernalia
...oid people who use drugs or alcohol
...void places where I used to use
☐ Attend 12-Step or support meetings
☐ Get a sponsor
☐ Schedule daily activities/keep busy
☐ Exercise daily (every minute counts)
☐ Pay off money I owe (even little by little)
☐ Work on my "addictive" behaviors
☐ Find a counselor and meet regularly
☐ Learn healthy ways to deal with stress

Congrats on each check! What will it take for you to start doing the starred options?

_____

_____

6. Got triggers? What types of things, places, and people make you vulnerable to relapse? Choose from the options below and add your own.

☐ Using friends and places
☐ Difficult people
☐ Problems and stress that wear me down.
☐ Painful feelings like anger or sadness
☐ Additional triggers:

☐ Places where I used to use
☐ Positive thoughts about drugs/alcohol
☐ Boredom
☐ Sometimes out of the blue

_____

_____

7. How will you deal with cravings and triggers? No matter how serious you are about recovery, you'll experience cravings and triggers. How will you deal with them?

☐ Identify cravings and urges
☐ Learn to avoid triggers
☐ Additional methods:

☐ Learn to distract away from cravings
☐ Learn trigger-busting skills

_____

_____

In this book, we'll spend plenty of time talking about making changes, learning new skills, getting past cravings & triggers, and loving life without drugs. In the meantime, turn the page and fill in the blank boxes with things you can do now to deal with cravings and triggers. Then go to page 8 for something completely different.

Fill in the boxes with things you can do now to deal with craving & triggers. Coloring is optional!

RECOVERY PLAN PART 2

SOMETHING COMPLETELY DIFFERENT.

Imagine you're walking through a forest. The flowers and leaves and butterflies flutter about, and a sunrise of a thousand colors lies just ahead. *What's this gotta do with recovery?* you think, but you keep walking – until you see it.

It's a box on a rock. The lid is shiny, the body a deep green, and there's writing on top:

> Ask one question about YOU, and
> we'll provide one answer about YOU.
> Open when ready. No payment required.

THE BOX

1.   You've found a box in the forest. It's waiting for your response. What do you do?

a. You stomp the box into pieces. You never trust boxes, especially ones you find in a forest.
b. You take the box home with you and rent it out, 100 bucks a pop.
c. You open the box.
d. You tell it to ask you questions. You already have all the answers.

2.   You choose C. The box opens with a rush of wind, ruffling your hair and clothes. You peer inside. What do you see?

a. A genie. It's blond, wears pink, has a stunning smile, and calls you Master.
b. A bright light. It's so bright you cover your eyes and still see light.
c. You don't see anything, but you hear your favorite song.
d. A deep hole and a rabbit.

3. The box groans. "What does it matter what you see? What is it you'd like to *know*?" Choose one of the following questions.

    a. Why did I choose recovery?
    b. Where have I been all these years?
    c. How do I deal with cravings and triggers?
    d. Who was I in my past life?
    e. How do I calm myself when I'm upset?
    f. How do I deal with problem thoughts?
    g. What is the meaning of life?
    h. What should I do during the day?
    i. How can I be a better friend?
    j. How do I communicate better?
    k. How do I remember my worth?
    l. Who wrote this book, anyway?

THE BOX II

Imagine you're a very informed alien sitting inside a box, and you have all the answers. You love sharing these answers, and you're always happy when a human comes along with a question. As usual, today's visitor needs to know something:

" _____ ?"

(Please write your question
from #3 on the line above)

You jump out of the box, sit on a nearby log, and cross your tentacles. What do you tell the human? Please write your answer in the space below.

Can't think of an answer? No worries. Simply go to the next page and find the box that corresponds to your question.

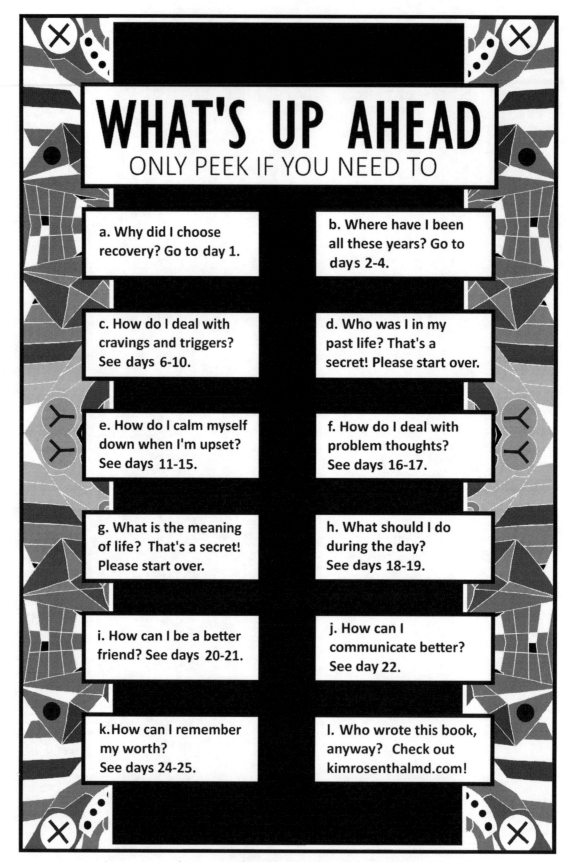

WHAT'S UP AHEAD
ONLY PEEK IF YOU NEED TO

a. Why did I choose recovery? Go to day 1.

b. Where have I been all these years? Go to days 2-4.

c. How do I deal with cravings and triggers? See days 6-10.

d. Who was I in my past life? That's a secret! Please start over.

e. How do I calm myself down when I'm upset? See days 11-15.

f. How do I deal with problem thoughts? See days 16-17.

g. What is the meaning of life? That's a secret! Please start over.

h. What should I do during the day? See days 18-19.

i. How can I be a better friend? See days 20-21.

j. How can I communicate better? See day 22.

k. How can I remember my worth? See days 24-25.

l. Who wrote this book, anyway? Check out kimrosenthalmd.com!

Answers to these questions can be found in the pages ahead.

DAYS 1-25

DAY 1: WHY RECOVERY?

PURPOSE OF THIS WORKSHEET:

- To compare life before and after quitting

1. SO YOU'VE QUIT USING! CONGRATS!

Now that you're clean and sober, why do you choose recovery? To make things easier, we've included a list of reasons below. Read through the list and check those that apply to you personally, then *cross out* all ridiculous or useless options.

REASONS TO CHOOSE RECOVERY	
Check those that apply to you and cross out all ridiculous or useless options.	
☐ To show my family I care	
☐ To be a better friend	
☐ To be a good example for others	
☐ To pass drug tests	
☐ To show myself I can stay clean	
☐ To do better at school or work	
☐ To do better at work	
☐ To avoid problems with the DEA	
☐ To grow a beard	
☐ To save money or avoid debt	☐ To replace drugs with gambling
☐ To stop getting into trouble	☐ To improve my appearance
☐ To fulfill the terms of my probation	☐ To reach for my goals and dreams
☐ To avoid homelessness	☐ To avoid psychiatric hospitals
☐ This isn't a reason. We're just making sure you've read all options.	☐ To avoid drama
☐ To avoid problems with the law	☐ To remember who I really am
☐ Because my spouse is worth it	☐ Because I believe sobriety is worth it

REASONS TO CHOOSE RECOVERY (CONTINUED)	
Check those that apply to you and cross out all ridiculous or useless options.	
☐ To make a difference in the world	☐ To safely purchase a DEA sniffer dog
☐ To not lose custody of my kids	☐ Because I'm sick of using
☐ To become a leader	☐ To stop hurting others
☐ To avoid DUI's	☐ To take revenge against my dealer
☐ For health reasons	☐ To help others with addiction
☐ To get rid of scaly skin	☐ To write a book about my recovery
☐ To embrace faith and meaning	☐ To lose tolerance so I can use again

Why else did you quit? Add three personal reasons.

ANSWERS

People quit for all sorts of reasons. The "right" answers will vary from person to person.

What are the ridiculous or useless options? The "This isn't a reason" option is a freebie, but there are more. People don't quit to specifically "grow a beard" (that has nothing to do with recovery), "replace drugs with gambling" (that's just another addiction), or "safely purchase a DEA sniffer dog" (although opinions will differ, and some DEA sniffer dogs are cute). Quitting to "take revenge against my dealer" isn't a good reason to quit. Quitting to "lose tolerance so I can use again" is dangerous.

On the other hand, choosing recovery to get rid of scaly skin might be helpful if quitting actually helps; we'll leave that up to you to decide. All others are serious reasons for quitting.

2. TWO PICTURES. There are two windows below, each looking into a different world. The first is the world of addiction, when you were still using. The second is now, since you quit. What do you see in each window? Grab some pencils or markers and draw. Don't groan!

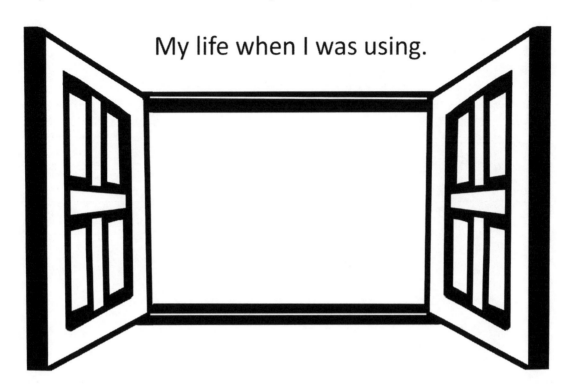

My life when I was using.

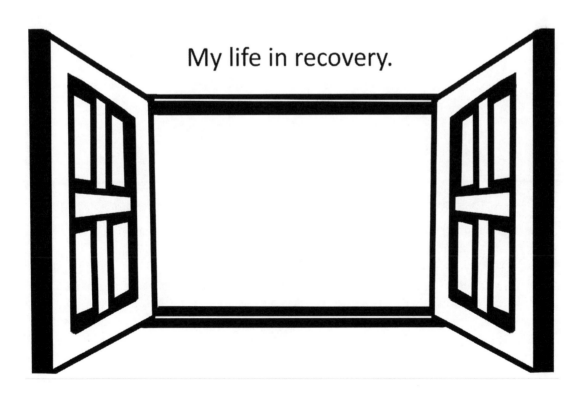

My life in recovery.

REFLECTION

Look at your "before" and "after" pictures. Explain in a few words what you see in each.

```
+-----------------------------+     +-----------------------------+
|                             |     |                             |
|                             |     |                             |
|                             |     |                             |
|                             |     |                             |
|                             |     |                             |
|                             |     |                             |
|                             |     |                             |
+-----------------------------+     +-----------------------------+
```

What differences did you notice between the two?

What surprised you about your drawings?

Chances are you didn't know ahead of time that drugs would cause problems. People don't wake up one day thinking, "Oh, I want to develop a substance use disorder now." But it happens, and it can happen to anyone. We don't always make the right decisions. But here's your chance to choose right. How? First, recognize that life with drugs *sucks*. Second, aim for a sober life you love. That's what this book is about. Welcome to recovery.

DAY 2. MEMORIES OF ADDICTION

PURPOSE OF THIS WORKSHEET:

- To better understand the role of addiction in your life

POETRY. Before we talk about recovery, we need to better understand your past and how drugs & alcohol affected you.

If addiction were a poem, would yours rhyme? You're going to pull together a poem about the pain of addiction. The trick is to capture the confusion and frustration and hurt on paper. This is your chance to complain. If you prefer, make it a song or rap or piece of fiction or essay… just write!

Before you start, there are two rules: (a) Avoid putting drugs in a positive light. Your writing should back up the reason you chose recovery. (b) You don't have to write about anything you prefer to avoid (like extremely painful experiences).

You'll use the next two pages to write your poem. Feel free to use lots of crazy imagery and colorful words. Play around with foreign expressions. Paste pictures. Add aromatherapy. Make it yours.

Here are questions to help you along:

1. What has addiction taken from you?

2. How has it hurt you?

3. How has it hurt others?

REFLECTION

Now that you've got addiction and its heartaches on paper, give it a happy ending. Use the space below to introduce recovery.

Most people would say that life with drugs hurts. You don't have to look far to hear this: Just do an online search for "poetry about addiction." This is a painful place to linger. Adding that positive ending is essential to recovery. In the next handout, Day 3, we'll explore your life on a broader scale, scanning for great memories too, to help you remember you're much more than a person with a substance use disorder.

If this exercise brought up a lot of ghosts, or worse, talk to someone you trust, preferably a professional. You can also call the NAMI Hotline at 1 800 950 NAMI.

TAKE A BREAK THE "NO" SIGN

Below, you'll find nine little fellows with nine signs. After reading each sign carefully, please determine which two match. The answer is on page 135.

SAY NO TO DRUGS.

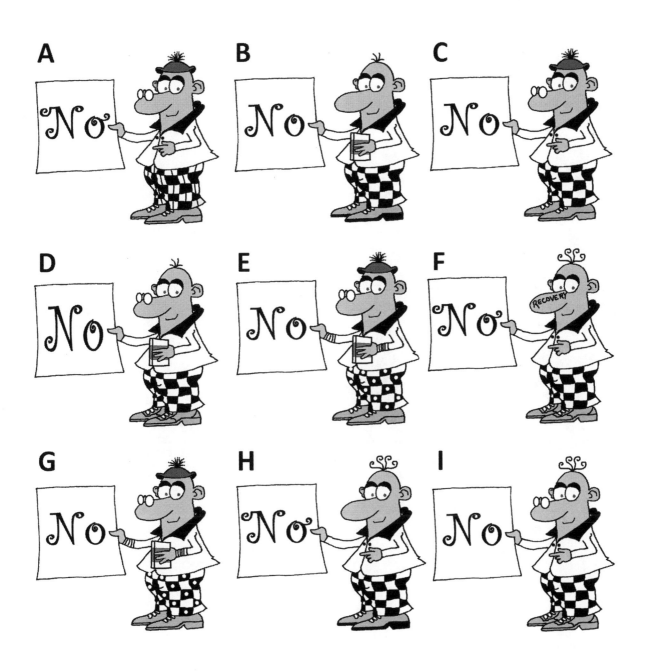

DAY 3. YOUR LIFE SO FAR

PURPOSE OF THIS WORKSHEET:

- To explore your journey from chemical dependency to the present
- To work on map-building skills, ha ha ha (Just kidding)

YOUR JOURNEY

To best know where you're going, it's important to understand both past triumphs and past problems. Start by filling in the boxes below. Later in this worksheet, you'll use this information to draw a map of your life.

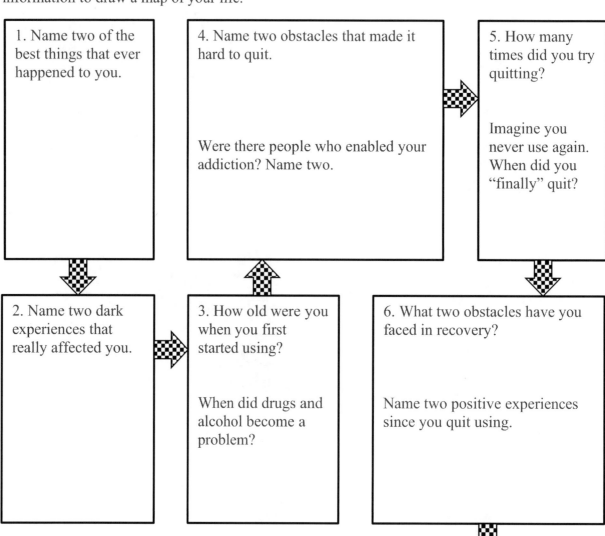

1. Name two of the best things that ever happened to you.

4. Name two obstacles that made it hard to quit.

Were there people who enabled your addiction? Name two.

5. How many times did you try quitting?

Imagine you never use again. When did you "finally" quit?

2. Name two dark experiences that really affected you.

3. How old were you when you first started using?

When did drugs and alcohol become a problem?

6. What two obstacles have you faced in recovery?

Name two positive experiences since you quit using.

7. Name two people who helped you get/stay clean. Then go to the next page.

RECOVERY MAP. Now that you've got all that info together, you're going to capture your story on paper by creating a personal recovery map. Here are your instructions.

1. You'll find a blank map of an island on the next page.
2. Draw a long, winding road on the map, from birth to where you are now. We recommend starting in pencil.
3. Add symbols to represent different parts of your life. See below for ideas.
4. Label the symbols and other important stuff with short phrases.
5. The map doesn't have to be perfect, but it must be yours!
6. For an example, see the sample map at the bottom of this page.

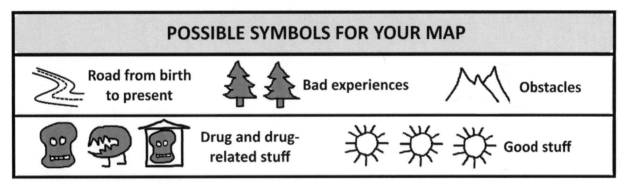

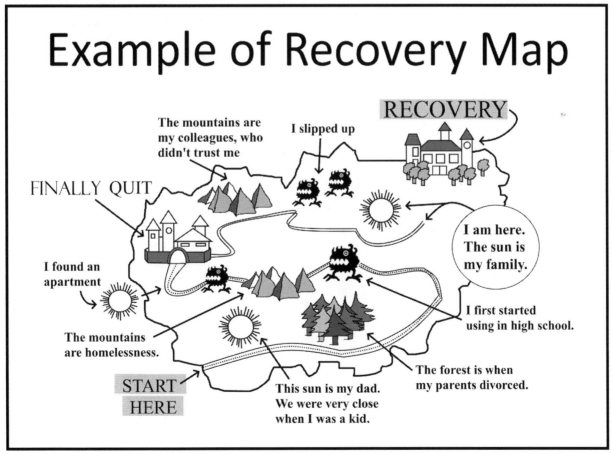

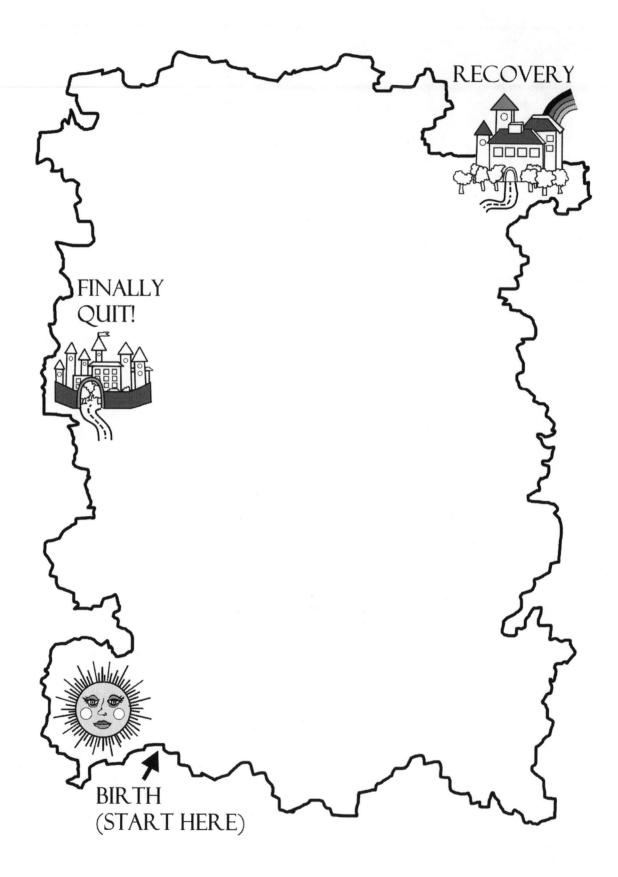

You're not quite finished. Go back to your map and circle all positive experiences with a red marker. Circle all negative experiences with a blue marker.

Is your map filled with more bad than good experiences? Sometimes we focus so much on the negative stuff that we forget the positive. Is there anything good you forgot to add? Please go back and add all the great stuff.

REFLECTION

As you drew your map, what about your life surprised you?

What bad experiences stick out? How have they helped you grow stronger?

What good experiences stick out? How have they helped you grow stronger?

DAY 4: SATISFIED WITH LIFE?

PURPOSE OF THIS WORKSHEET:

- To better appreciate what's going right
- To recognize where more work is needed

1. RATE LIFE SATISFACTION.

In prior worksheets, we've looked at your past, i.e. what's happened until now. But how are things today? Please rate your current life satisfaction in the following categories. Choose a number between (1) Very Dissatisfied and (10) Very Satisfied.

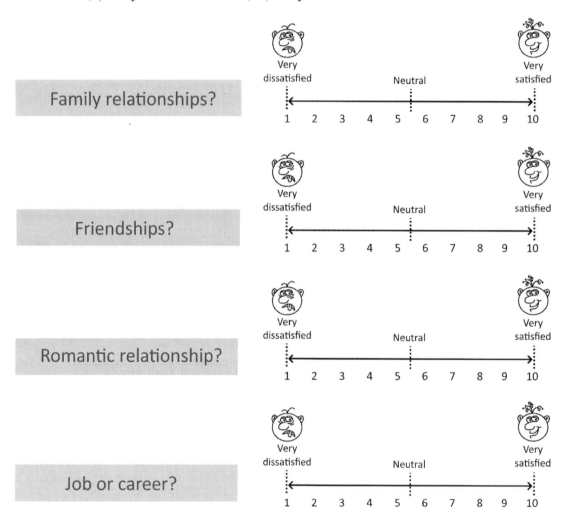

Continued: Please rate your satisfaction for each category, choosing a number between (1) Very Dissatisfied and (10) Very Satisfied.

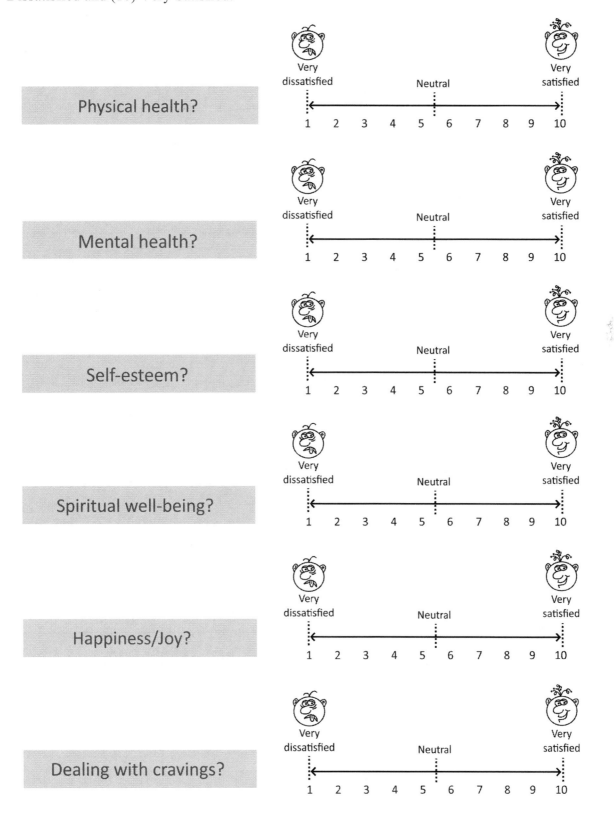

2. LETTING GO OF THE BAD STUFF

Looking over the last two pages, what parts of your life did you rate the lowest?

Recovery promises a life worth living, if you're willing to stick with it. The trick is to let go of the bad stuff and make room for what helps you grow. What bad stuff are you holding onto? Check the ideas that apply to you and add your own below.

☐ Grief over the loss of addiction   ☐ Traumatic experiences
☐ Painful or toxic relationships   ☐ Problems with anger
☐ Bad things I've done   ☐ Guilt, shame, or low self-esteem
☐ People I've lost or pushed away   ☐ Failures and disappointments
☐ Not finishing school   ☐ Losing my car
☐ Feeling depressed or anxious   ☐ Drugs/alcohol
☐ Other bad stuff I'm holding onto:

"Getting rid of the bad stuff" can mean a lot of things: processing a mistake, getting help for a problem, paying back debt, making amends with someone you hurt, finding peace symbolically, or consciously letting yourself move on. What can you do now to let go of the bad? Answer in the space below.

3. HOLDING ONTO THE GOOD STUFF

Looking over the last two pages, what's going well in your life?

What are the good things in your life? Read through the options below and check the ideas that sound right to you, then add your own below.

☐ My family and friends are supportive.   ☐ I'm positive and hopeful about the future
☐ I feel confident in my relationship   ☐ My faith keeps me going
☐ I've got a good job   ☐ I go to 12-step meetings often
☐ I'm studying something worthwhile   ☐ I enjoy my life. It's fun being me.
☐ My creativity gives me energy   ☐ I believe in myself.
☐ I'm in good physical health   ☐ I'm resilient and deal with stress well.
☐ Other good things in my life:

What can you do now to promote well-being and recovery in your life? Answer in the space below.

REFECTION

This worksheet is about hope. Life isn't always easy, but if you adjust your life to let go of unhealthy things, if instead you seek the healthy and worthwhile, you just might find yourself closer to where you want to be.

To emphasize the importance of HOPE, we offer the image below. We're not sure how many *hopes* you'll find in the picture, but there are six extra words. Please find them and put them in a meaningful order to complete the following anonymous phrase. The answer is on page 135.

"HAVE HOPE….

_____ _____ _____ _____ _____ _____

DAY 5. BEAUTY OF BEING YOU

Purpose of this worksheet:

- To remember the importance of self-compassion

Chances are you've made mistakes, but you've also overcome great obstacles. Give yourself a pat on the back and complete the following phrases. If you can't think of answers, jot down how you'd *like* to be.

1.   Three compliments people have given me...

2.   Three things I'm good at...

3. Three things I've overcome…

4. Three things I like about my looks…

5. Three things I like about my character…

6. Three things that make me different or unique…

7. Three good things I've done for other people…

Reflection

Recovery means many things. One important part is self-compassion. How can you be kinder to yourself?

If you don't believe the statements you wrote, how can you change that?

Sometimes self-esteem and identity are crushed under the weight of past mistakes and bad decisions, regardless of whether those decisions were yours or someone else's. If you can't find anything positive to say about yourself, be kind and treat yourself as you would a friend. Healthy recovery means taking care of yourself.

TAKE A BREAK. BRAIN STUFF

We're not sure what's going on with these brains, but can you find the nine differences between them? The answer is on page 136.

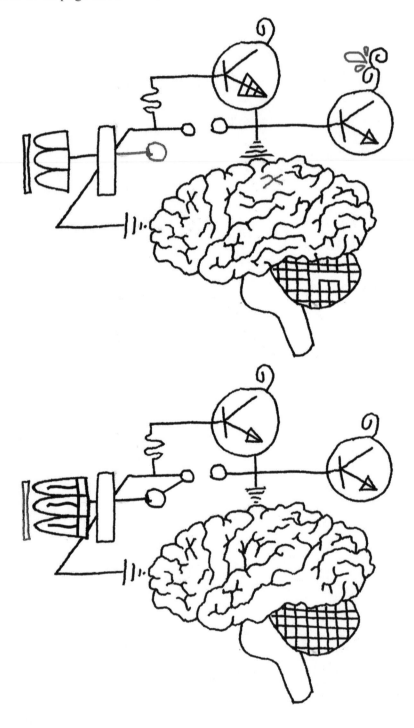

DAY 6. DEALING WITH CRAVINGS 1

PURPOSE OF THIS HANDOUT

- To learn about and survive cravings

CRAVINGS

Okay, a quick quiz. Circle True or False.

1. True   False   When a person has a craving, they have lots of time to reflect and make an informed decision about whether to use or not.

2. True   False   Cravings are a sign of weakness.

3. True   False   Cravings mean you're not serious about recovery.

4. True   False   Cravings become less frequent the longer you are in recovery.

5. True   False   Cravings are always caused by a trigger.

6. True   False   You should plan how to deal with cravings before they happen.

7. True   False   The best way to say NO to cravings is to practice saying NO.

ANSWERS

Here's the spiel.

Sometimes, when you've gone too long without using, your brain notices there's something missing. It's used to having drugs or alcohol present, and yep, that's when you get a craving.

Cravings are normal for people in recovery. Having them doesn't mean you're weak or lazy.

The problem is that, when cravings happen, you often aren't in a position to make good decisions. It's important to plan ahead: What will you do when cravings happen?

The good news is they don't last long (usually minutes), and they get less frequent and less intense as recovery progresses.

Cravings can show up out of the blue, but often there's a trigger lurking nearby. A trigger is anything that makes you more likely to use. See pages 50-57 to learn more about triggers. First spiel over. Please go to the next page.

> The problem is that, when
>
> # CRAVINGS
>
> happen, you aren't usually in a position to make an informed decision. It's important to plan ahead: what will you do when they come up?

DO'S AND DON'TS OF CRAVINGS

Below you'll find some helpful ideas about dealing with cravings, but someone really messed up. It's a mess. Please help us decipher each sentence. Much appreciated.

The following sentences have no spaces. Rewrite each idea in the space below... with spaces.

When dealing with cravings, DO more of the following:

1. Avoidalltriggers:Ifthere'ssomethingtriggeringthecraving,runawaynow.

2. Exercisemore:It'sagooddistractionandreducesstressandanxiety,andit'sgoodforyou.

3. Relax:Learnhowtododeepbreathingexercisesormeditate.Levitatationcanbehelpfultoo.

4. Hobby:Replacedruguseandcravingswithsomethingbeneficialorfun.

5. Self-talk:Don'ttalkyourselfintousingordrinking.Becarefulwhatyouthink!

6. Patience:Rememberthatcravingsdon'tlast.

In the sentences below, there are spaces where spaces don't belong. Please rewrite each idea, preferably something in English.

When dealing with cravings, DON'T do the following:

7. Don'trep laced rugswi thadd ictivebe hav iorsa ndbadh abits.

8. Do n'tkeepus ingord rink ingaft ermes sing upo nce

9. Do n'tma keyo urlifem ore stressful.Fi xba ddec isio ns.Learncop in gski lls.

10. Don'tgi veint ope erpres sure.

Here's the take-home message. Rearrange word order to help the message make sense.

Remember these final points.

11. normal over Cravings weaker are and time get.

12. deal with to The have way a to cravings plan ahead of best time is.

See page 35 for answers.

ANSWERS FROM PAGE 34

When dealing with cravings, DO more of the following:

1.Avoidalltriggers:Ifthere'ssomethingtriggeringthecraving,runawaynow.
Avoid all triggers: If there's something triggering the craving, run away now.

2.Exercisemore:It'sagooddistractionandreducesstressandanxiety,andit'sgoodforyou.
Exercise more: It's a good distraction and reduces stress and anxiety, and it's good for you.

3.Relax:Learnhowtododeepbreathingexercisesormeditate.Levitatationcanbehelpfultoo.
Relax: Learn how to do deep breathing exercises or meditate. Levitation can be helpful too (please laugh).

4.Hobby:Replacedruguseandcravingswithsomethingbeneficialorfun.
Hobby: Replace drug use and cravings with something beneficial or fun.

5.Self-talk:Don'ttalkyourselfintousingordrinking.Becarefulwhatyouthink!
Self-talk: Don't talk yourself into using or drinking. Be careful what you think!

6.Patience:Rememberthatcravingsdon'tlast.
Patience: Remember that cravings don't last.

DON'T do the following:

7. Don'trep laced rugswi thadd ictivebe hav iorsa ndbadh abits.
Don't replace drugs with addictive behaviors and bad habits.

8. Do n'tkeepus ingord rink ingaft ermes sing upo nce
Don't keep using or drinking after messing up once.

9. Do n'tma keyo urlifem ore stressful.Fi xba ddec isio ns.Learncop in gski lls.
Don't make your life more stressful. Fix bad decisions. Learn coping skills.

10. Don'tgi veint ope erpres sure.
Don't give into peer pressure.

Remember these final points.

11. normal over Cravings weaker are and time get.
Cravings are normal and get weaker over time.

12. deal with to The have way a to cravings plan ahead of best time is.
The best way to deal with cravings is to have a plan ahead of time.

URGE MANAGEMENT TECHNIQUES

here are dozens of ways to deal with cravings. You'll find some below. Match each technique to the examples on page 37.

URGE MANAGEMENT TECHNIQUES

Say NO. Put NO on speed-dial. Check out pages 39-43.

Ridiculous Name. Give the craving a strange name and talk to it. "Oh, you're back again, Evil One? Allow me to laugh at your useless efforts, ha ha ha!" Write a dialogue.

Pause & Distract. Distract yourself until the cravings are gone. Do something that has nothing to do with the urge to use. What can you do to distract yourself?

The DANG Method. Combines all three of the above methods onto one sheet of paper... plus coloring. See pages 46-49.

Reach Out & Touch. Call or visit someone you trust. Consider going to a 12-Step meeting.

Mindfulness. Find calmness and well-being by focusing on the present. See pages 66-69.

Surf the Urge. Focus on the craving and its sensation until it goes away. Extra points for journaling the experience.

MATCH EXAMPLES BELOW TO TECHNIQUES ON PAGE 36

Below you'll find examples of people dealing with cravings. Match each character below to a technique listed on page 36. Some techniques are used twice.

LANCE

took his craving "Pickles" to the theater, put it up on the stage, and watched it closely. It wiggled twice then fell over dead. The craving was gone!

KARY

was an excellent meditator, so much that in her efforts to put aside a craving, she could float four feet above the ground. Jump as it tried, the craving couldn't reach her.

CARLOS

had a huge diary, where he kept notes about his cravings: what they felt like, when they came and went, and what he did to distract himself.

JAMAL

his craving followed him around, a funny-looking crocodile he called "Crocker Reptile And Pincushion" (C.R.A.P.). The craving was so offended, it disappeared one night and was never seen again.

JILL

wanted to marry Jack, but she knew she couldn't quit with him around. The conversation went like this: "Will you marry me?" Her answer: "NO NO NO NO NO NO NO NO NO NO..."

ANSWERS TO EXAMPLES & TECHNIQUES

Lance – Ridiculous name
Kary – Mindful meditation
Carlos – Surf the urge, pause and distract
Jamal – Ridiculous name
Jill—Say no

REFLECTION

Warning: This paragraph contains triggers for cravings.

Triggering situation: Imagine you're sitting on a bus in some distant country. No one speaks English, and everything is colorful and cheap. You're hungry, and your little sister is sitting next to you eating an enormous slice of carrot cake with milk. Just ahead, there's a lad puffing at a cigarette. The white-haired woman next to him flails her arms dramatically, sipping at her vodka and talking about something you don't understand. The friendly set of twins behind you are….

Whatever your weakness, there's someone on this bus giving you cravings. How can you use the urge management techniques listed in this handout to deal with them?

DAY 7. DEALING WITH CRAVINGS 2

PURPOSE OF THIS HANDOUT

- To better understand cravings
- To practice saying NO

CRAVINGS. Cravings are intense urges to drink or use drugs. They can be overpowering, especially early in recovery, so you have to come up with an anti-craving game plan. But first, here are some random questions.

You're on a date with Perfection. You've just met, but it's clear they're the love of your life. The way they move, the way they watch you, it's meant to be… until they speak. "So we're going to rob a bank tonight?" They're not kidding. What do you say?

a. Absolutely. I love you.
b. How much we gonna rob?
c. Anything you want, love.
d. No.

The right answer is D. The love of your life smiles a stunning smile. "Okay, we'll start with something smaller… steal a car?" What do you say?

a. Which car?
b. How many cars?
c. Anything you want, love.
d. No.

The right answer is still D. Your date looks at you disapprovingly. "Shoplift a piece of gum?" What do you say?

a. Which flavor?
b. Where, when, and how often?
c. Anything you want, love.
d. No.

Again, we hope you chose D. Oh, but your perfect date isn't finished. They're still trying to tempt you into a life of crime. "Jaywalking? Can we go jaywalking?" What do you say?

a. No.
b. No.
c. No.
d. All of the above.

D (all of the above) is right, of course. Congratulations, you passed Round One.

SAYING NO

Welcome to the "NO" method for handling cravings. Also called "Thought-Stopping," the "Stop Sign Method," and "Broken Record," the ability to plant a big fat NO on top of an urge is a powerful tool.

How does it work? Cravings don't last long. Faced with an urge, think NO. Think NO again and again and again, and keep doing this until the craving backs off. There are many ways to do this.

- Imagine NO is a sheep. Think of sheep jumping past you one at a time, frolicking happily as they… okay, that one doesn't work. Skip sheep.

- Imagine NO is a stop sign. Focus on counting a bunch of stop signs, one at a time, until the craving has subsided.

- Imagine different variations of NO. Try "Nope," "Nah," "No way," "Sorry," "Certainly not," "Absolute negativity," "By no means," and "I shalt not." Don't forget, "You're kidding, right?" If you're up to it, vary volume, speed, even language – and just say NO.

By now you've got "NO" memorized. You're an expert No-Sayer, fast at the draw, but that doesn't mean you'll say it at the right time   This might sound strange, but the best way to say NO is to practice ahead of time. Don't rely on will power when the moment comes.

Repeat after us: NO. NO. NO. NO. NO. NO. NO. Thanks.

JUST SAY NO: A THEATER PRODUCTION

To better emphasize the role of "NO" in your life and help you prepare for future bouts of cravings, you're going to write a play. No worries! All that means is you're going to write a conversation between YOU and CRAVING. Balance serious efforts with a bit of goofiness, and you'll be just fine.

Think of a high-risk situation that gives you cravings, a scenario where you'll need to say NO. Describe that situation here.

Step One. → **Who plays who? Choose two actors or create your own.**

Who represents YOU in your play?   Who represents the CRAVING?

- ☐ Some Great Hero   ☐ Some Great Villain
- ☐ Yoda from Star Wars   ☐ Q from Star Trek
- ☐ You yourself in your situation   ☐ The thing that's tempting you (literally)
- ☐ The Infamous Madam Recovery   ☐ That Rearing-to-Go Relapse Dude
- ☐ Your idea: ☐ Your idea:

Step Two. → **What is the setting of your play? Choose one or create your own.**

- ☐ The scene is a dark alley. There's a loud boom-boom in the air suggesting a party nearby.
- ☐ The play takes place in a small apartment. It's overwhelmingly messy and smells like stale cigarette smoke.
- ☐ The scene is a 50-foot yacht that's moored to a private dock. It's flanked by an enormous mansion with frolicking horses in the distance.
- ☐ Your idea:

Step Three. → **Get the general story on paper. Answer the following questions.**

What are YOU doing before CRAVING shows up?

CRAVING steps onto the scene. What does it want YOU to do?

How does it tempt YOU? What does the urge promise?

Why should you turn CRAVING down?

Step Four. → **Imagine YOU and the CRAVING together in your scene of choice.**

How does the conversation start: small-talk, sweetness, or words as sharp as spears? Who speaks first? What do they say? What happens after that? Go onto the next page and tell a story, making sure to give yourself extra credit each time you say NO.

YOUR FRIENDLY "just say no" THEATER PRODUCTION

Use the space below to write your "JUST SAY NO" play.

REFLECTION

Did your theater production end on a positive note? If not, please write a happy ending in the space below!

"Practicing NO" might sound like child's play, but it can make the difference between relapse and recovery. What other situations do you have in your life where you should say NO? List three and place a couple NO's next to each one.

Great, that's it. Just say NO!

SOMEWHERE IN A DISTANT GALAXY…

(There's the sound of forced breathing. Enter Darth Vader and Luke Skywalker.)

~~DARTH VADER~~ CRAVING (in a super low voice): Luke, you're meant to fulfill your destiny. If only you knew the power of the Dark Side.

~~LUKE~~ YOU: Luke? Who's Luke? Naw, man, that ain't me.

CRAVING: Luke, I am your father.

YOU: No, you're not.

CRAVING: The Dark Side is in our blood. Join me, and the power will be ours!

YOU: No, like I said, you've got the wrong guy.

CRAVING: Oh?

YOU: Yeah, my name is Paul.

CRAVING: Paul? Uh, Paul… you wanna join the Dark Side?

YOU: No.

CRAVING: The Dark Side is a pathway to many abilities. You need to fulfill your destiny. You're meant to stand by my side and…

YOU: No.

CRAVING: No?

YOU: No.

CRAVING: Please?

YOU: Nope, nah, absolute negativity.

(Craving sighs and walks away defeated. You wink at the audience and bow.) END

TAKE A BREAK, PUZZLES THAT SAY NO

Say NO to addiction! Here are various exercises in negation. The answers are on page 137.

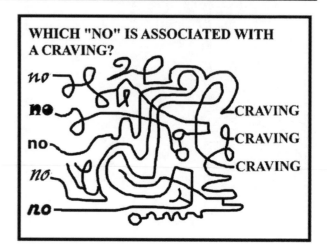

PLEASE SOLVE THIS "NO" MAZE.

START HERE   **END**

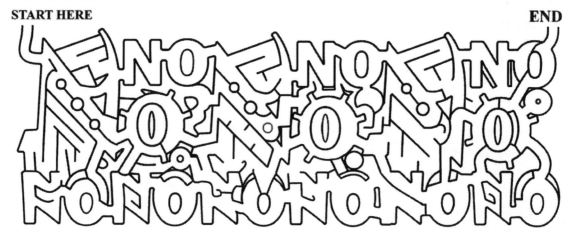

How many stop signs (octagons) are there in each picture?

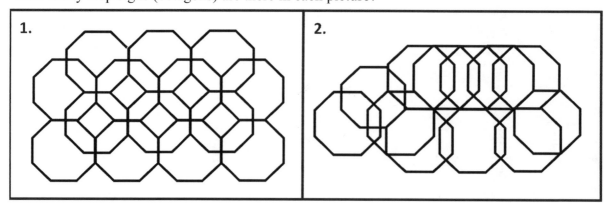

Please reflect on NO while adding color or ink spots to the following picture.

DAY 8. DEALING WITH CRAVINGS 3

PURPOSE OF THIS HANDOUT

- To memorize and practice the D.A.N.G. Technique for getting past cravings

WHAT ARE CRAVINGS?

A craving (or urge) is a desire to use drugs or alcohol. Cravings make you more vulnerable to using and relapse, so it's important to have an "urge-management technique" (or techniques) in your pocket before you face them. The good news is that urges don't last long, and they lose their power as you get further along in recovery.

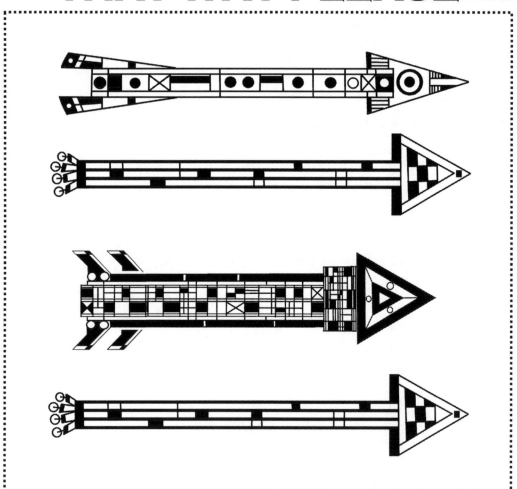

Please go to the next page.

THE D.A.N.G URGE-MANAGEMENT TECHNIQUE

Combining SMART Recovery's DISARM, early awareness, saying NO, and the wonders of distraction, here's the DANG technique. It's meant to help get you past those dang cravings.

THE D.A.N.G.
URGE-MANAGEMENT
TECHNIQUE
AN IMPORTANT PART OF RECOVERY

Different name . Replace the word "craving" or "urge" with a new name--something strong, meaningful, and possibly funny. This puts it in perspective and can help reduce its power over you. Consider names like Alcohol Salesman, That Political Mess, My Problem Friend, or Gerflushenheimer.

What name do you choose? _____

Aware it's happening. Recognize the urge when it starts and deal with it as soon as possible.
How can you tell _____ has shown up? Check those that apply:
NAME OF YOUR CRAVING

- ☐ Thinking about using/want to use
- ☐ Start looking for reasons to contact using friends
- ☐ Recovery seems boring or too much work

- ☐ Feel like drugs aren't a problem
- ☐ What are your personal warning symptoms?

No, no, no. Put "NO" on speed dial. The moment you sense _____ has shown up, say NO.
NAME OF YOUR CRAVING

Say NO repeatedly. Don't even consider using. If you're alone, strike a pose, flail your arms, and say NO ten times. Extra credit for saying it in Russian. Just say NO!

Got distraction? If the craving (or whatever it's called) is strong enough, set your timer for 30 minutes and do something to distract yourself. Here are some ideas:

- ☐ Call someone
- ☐ Go to a meeting
- ☐ Go for a walk
- ☐ Text a friend
- ☐ Doodle a pic

- ☐ Make a ring out of a dollar bill
- ☐ Google funny-looking fish
- ☐ Fill in all the O's on this page
- ☐ Put on music and dance
- ☐ Find new apps for your phone

If the cravings don't go away, repeat the distraction.

WHAT'S THE D.A.N.G. METHOD?

DANG is a set of urge-busting techniques piled together. The purpose is to help you remember options when you need them. You can use one at a time – or all four. DANG stands for *"Different name," "Aware it's happening," "No, no, no,'* and *"Got distraction?"* We'll talk you through each technique.

1. Different Name

Like the SMART Recovery DISARM method, DANG gives the craving a ridiculous name. Assigning it a name separates the craving from the essence of you, allows you to examine it from a distance, and takes away some of its power. Assign a name before the craving starts, and add a catch-phrase if it helps: "Ahhh, there's Gerflushenheimer, that dang craving!"

2. Aware it's Happening

Now that you can see the craving more clearly, The D.A.N.G. method emphasizes the importance of catching the craving early. Early recognition gives you a chance to deal with it before it gains power. What are your warning signs that you've got an urge on the rise? Look internally and externally. It might be a thought or change in attitude, something in your environment, a physical sensation, even a memory cropping up.

> "I always get a craving when I hear this song. I can feel it in my face. Cigarettes start to look good, and I wanna go buy some."

3. No No No

As a third step, DANG means having the word NO on autopilot. Put a big fat NO over the craving and what you crave and do so repeatedly until it passes → or go onto #4.

> No no no no no no no no no no no no no no no no no no no
> Away with You!

4. Got Distraction?

If the craving is still around, top it off with 30 minutes of distraction. The DANG sheet on page 47 has some suggestions. See the list on page 88 for more ideas. If you still have cravings after that time, distract yourself another 30 minutes.

WHICH START FINISHES THE MAZE?

START #1

The answer is on page 138.

START #2

START #3

START #4

START #5

START #6

END

REFLECTION

Warning: The next paragraph contains triggers for cravings.

Triggering situation: You're driving home and make a wrong turn. Now you're in Canada, and everything is in French. You don't speak French. To make matters worse, you run out of gas, you lose all your money, your car is stolen, and then you sprain your little finger. You end up fighting for a stowaway spot on a train back to America, but then suddenly everything is in Japanese. You don't speak Japanese. So you're stressed, at risk for relapse. How can you use the DANG method to deal with the cravings?

Write your answer in the space below, using "You" instead of "I" and describing the experience like a story.

In this worksheet, we introduced four tools to help you deal with cravings. They can be done individually or in combination. *Memorize* the DANG Method and let it rescue you when you need it. In the next two worksheets, we'll take on triggers.

DAY 9. RECOGNIZING TRIGGERS

PURPOSE OF THIS HANDOUT

- To identify the triggers in your life

How do YOU deal with triggers?

1. TRIGGERS. Triggers are things that make people want to use. They can be a person, place, item, emotion, thought… just about anything. If you suddenly feel an urge to use, chances are there's a trigger nearby, even if you aren't aware of it. How do you handle a trigger? That's what Days 9 and 10 are about.

But first, we've got a few questions for you.

1. You're standing on a train track when you see a train coming your way. Assuming the train is a trigger, what do you do?

   a. You're all powerful. You roll up your sleeves and wait for the train to arrive, at which point you'll wrestle it to a stop. You've never wrestled a train before, of course, but you try not to think about that.
   b. You step off the tracks and keep a distance. Better to stay away from such nonsense.
   c. You can't help yourself. It's mesmerizing. You stand in place and wait for it to arrive. So the train just might kill you, but the experience will be worth it.
   d. You calculate the distance between the train and you. It has enough room to stop before it hits you. Staying put and certain, you pull out a phone, call the train conductor, and explain the situation. The train must be stopped… and immediately. You know it won't stop, but you act like you know what you're doing.

2. You're an expert diver in front of a crowd of millions. You're about to jump into the pool below when you notice there's a shark. It's a great white shark, and it's watching you. Assuming the shark is a trigger, what do you do?

   a. You turn around and get off the diving board. That trigger isn't worth your life.
   b. You've never been bitten by a shark before. That means you'll *never* get bitten by a shark. Therefore, the pool is perfectly safe. You dive off the board and get eaten by the shark.
   c. You know the shark is going to bite you, but hell, everyone has to die sometime. Might as well jump.
   d. You stand and watch the shark carefully. You realize it's a mermaid, not a shark, and she's stunning. You take a giant leap, ready to embrace this beautiful creature, and you get eaten by a shark.

2. ANSWERS

These questions emphasize the importance of recognizing (and avoiding) triggers, especially in early recovery. But trains and sharks aren't usual triggers. Please go back and cross out the words "train" and "shark" and replace them with "trigger." Then reread. Seriously!

Here are the answers.

1. B is your best option. Get away! A and D are dead ends; you've convinced yourself you can stop a train, which you can't, so you get run over. They're examples of false logic. C involves glamorizing trains, i.e. forgetting all the damage they've done to you in the past. It's a form of denial.

2. A is correct. The other options are excuses to use. They're examples of messed-up thinking. B is "I've never had a problem with drugs, which means I'll never have a problem." C, "We all have to die of something." Neither B nor C promote recovery. D glamorizes the shark into something pretty, a type of denial.

3. IDENTIFYING TRIGGERS

It's important to know your triggers, as you'll need to consciously deal with them as your recovery progresses.

(a) Triggers can be divided into internal and external types.

TYPES OF TRIGGERS

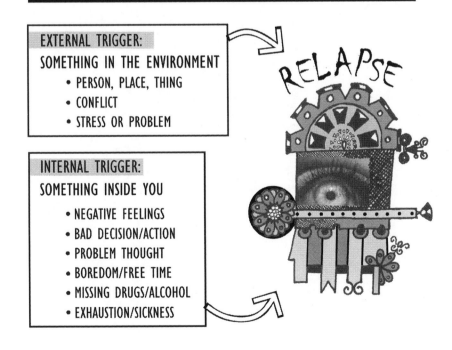

EXTERNAL TRIGGER:
SOMETHING IN THE ENVIRONMENT
- PERSON, PLACE, THING
- CONFLICT
- STRESS OR PROBLEM

INTERNAL TRIGGER:
SOMETHING INSIDE YOU
- NEGATIVE FEELINGS
- BAD DECISION/ACTION
- PROBLEM THOUGHT
- BOREDOM/FREE TIME
- MISSING DRUGS/ALCOHOL
- EXHAUSTION/SICKNESS

RELAPSE

(b) You can also identify triggers by the cravings they cause: next time you have an urge to use, consider what set it off. Pay attention! Scan for internal and external cues. More often than not, there's a trigger standing close by.

(c) You'll find a list of common triggers at the bottom of this page. Circle any that sound familiar, then see if you can find all terms in the word search. Answers are on page 139.

TRIGGER WORD SEARCH

```
F E E L I N G I N A D E Q U A T E T E U
A R D B A R S A N D C L U B S Y H U H S
P S R G H U K H T F V N M O Y R D W N I
S A R X E Y E N O M E V I S S E C X E N
L O R G H U K H T F V N M O Y R D W N G
O E N A B L E R S V Y U I O S D A D E H
N M H O P O S D A D E M E L B O R P Y A
E I C E A H D F V N M O Y R S D A S D N
L M O D I G E C N E D I F N O C R E V G
I I N W N E N R D H U K F V N M O Y R O
N E F C R E I D N C R E E M S D A E D U
E Y L D E M A C A A D E M Y O N C R E T
S F I S D A L H U K L S D A Z D C R E S
S F C O S D A D E Q E I C R E C E D E M
R M T F V N M O Y R Y Z A S D A B R E B
A C C E S S T O D R U G S H U K H U O A
U C T O O M U C H S T R E S S D E M I B
```

EXAMPLES OF TRIGGERS

Access to drugs
Bars and clubs
Boredom
Conflict
Denial

Enablers
Excessive money
Feeling inadequate
Loneliness

Pain
Paraphernalia
Problem
Too much stress

4. IDENTIFYING YOUR TRIGGERS

What are *your* triggers? Consider both external and internal. Write a list here.

REFLECTION

Why is it important to recognize your triggers?

Review your list of triggers. Pick three and describe each in detail. Consider all aspects: Is it internal or external? How often do you see it? How does it make you feel? What does it look like? What does it sound like or say?

We've talked a lot about identifying triggers, but how do you deal with them? Check out Day 10 for some answers.

DAY 10. GETTING PAST TRIGGERS

PURPOSE OF THIS HANDOUT

- To learn ways to deal with triggers, including avoiding them!

1. AVOIDING TRIGGERS

There are two healthy ways to manage triggers.

- Avoid them
- Deal with them

To emphasize the importance of avoiding triggers, especially in early recovery, please read the instructions in the box below and complete the task. Think "AVOID TRIGGER" as you do it! What's the take home message about avoidance? When it comes to dealing with triggers, avoiding them is your first plan of action. You want to put distance between the trigger and you, which means… slapping a big, fat NO on top of it.

AVOID TRIGGER

Rearrange the letters in the phrase, "AVOID TRIGGER,"
to create new words. How many can you find?

_____
_____
_____
_____
_____
_____
_____
_____
_____

Stumped? Here are a few freebies.
Just unscramble before adding them to your list.

GRTEA   TOG   RVERDI   RIA   DEIRAR   EDR   OGD

We've included more words in the Answer Section, page 139.

Turn the page for an interesting picture.

2. AN INTERESTING PICTURE

There are two healthy ways to deal with triggers. If faced with a trigger, please go to #1 (avoid the trigger) or #2 (deal with the trigger). #3 is bad news.

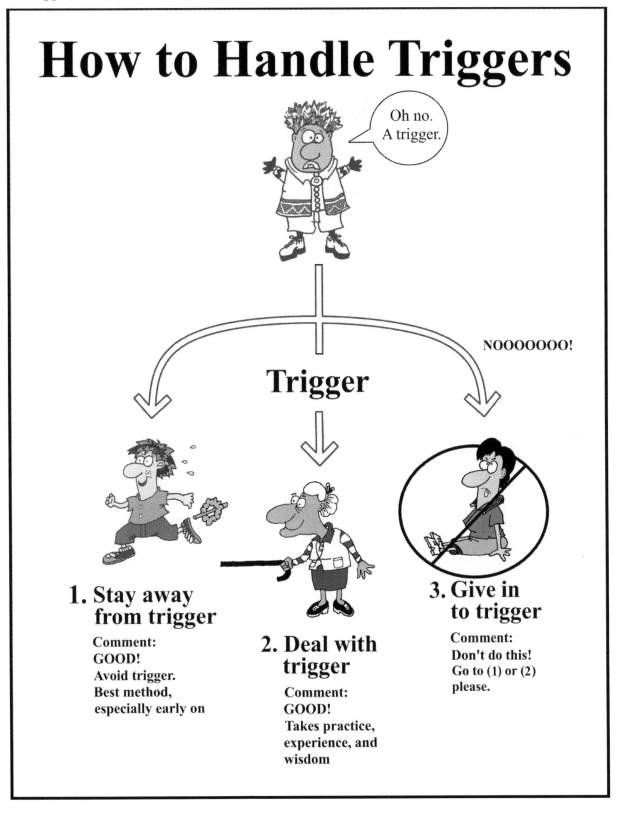

3. HOW DO YOU DEAL WITH TRIGGERS?

Triggers can't always be avoided. The good news is they lose their power over time. Even better, you have hundreds of trigger-busting strategies at your disposal. If one method doesn't help, try another. Below you'll find a bunch of good and ways to deal with urges to use. Circle all good options and cross out all bad ones.

LIST OF TRIGGER-BUSTING STRATEGIES	
Instructions: Circle all good strategies and cross out all bad ones.	
a. Distract yourself	b. Learn to calm yourself down
c. Problem-solve	d. Plan how to deal with it ahead of time
e. Just say NO	f. Worry yourself to death
g. Radically accept and decide not to use	h. Change how you think about it
i. Use optimism/positive psychology	j. Change how you act because of it
k. Blame others	l. Think about the consequences
m. Get rid of or destroy trigger*	n. Review reasons you want to stay clean
o. Go to 12-step meeting/talk to somebody	p. Go gambling
q. Write in your journal	r. Educate yourself about the trigger
s. Pray or read the Bible	t. Learn about getting high
u. Use imagery/imagination to stay clean	v. Take medications for cravings
w. Use it as an excuse to relapse	x. Buy a large teddy bear to cuddle
y. Hang out with non-using friends	z. Use urge management skills

* As usual, avoid injuring people or destroying property. And no harm to animals.

ANSWERS.

F, K, P, T, and W are bad ways to deal with triggers. As for right, M (get rid of/destroy trigger) is a good option in certain situations: you need to get rid of paraphernalia, "using souvenirs," contact information for using friends, and any drugs/alcohol in your possession. X (buy a teddy bear) might work for some, won't for others. The rest are healthy ways to deal with triggers.

REFLECTION

Try to prepare for potential triggers ahead of time.

Identify an unavoidable trigger that might be waiting for you up ahead. Describe three ways you can manage the trigger, Plans A, B, and C. After reading the example below, complete the chart at the bottom.

Example:

What if you're dealing with a cousin who's always making fun of your recovery? He belittles your efforts and says even an imbecile can stay clean. You get frustrated when you see him and always lose your temper. When you're that pissed off, you think you need drugs to calm down. You're going to bump into him at the family reunion this weekend. What do you do? Here are some ideas:

→Use deep breathing and muscle relaxation to keep control
→Remind yourself he lost his mother to alcohol; his issue has nothing to do with you.
→Bring a friend or two along for support
→Have a friend text or call you at the right time to get away from him, say after ten minutes.
→Refuse to acknowledge him if he gets offensive.

SURVIVE-A-TRIGGER PLANNER
Describe one unavoidable trigger you're likely to encounter this week.
Plan A: What trigger-busting strategy might help?
If Plan A doesn't work, what's Plan B?
If Plan B doesn't work, what's Plan C?

TAKE A BREAK.

DIFFERENT ROADS TO RECOVERY

There are 15 differences between these two images. Can you find them? The answers are on page 140.

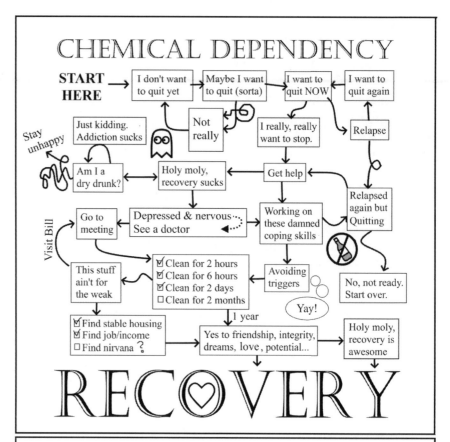

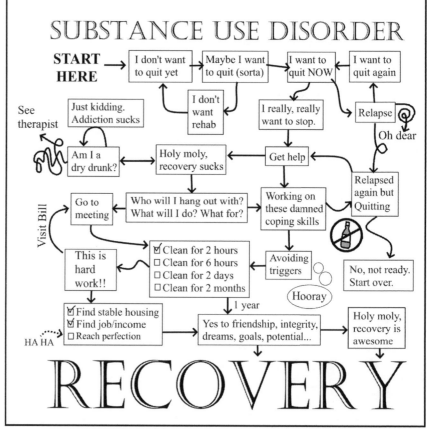

DAY 11. COPING SKILLS

PURPOSE OF THIS WORKSHEET:

- To introduce survival strategies, or coping skills
- To recognize the difference between good and bad skills

SURVIVAL SKILLS BASICS. Consider the following questions.

1. What are coping skills?

    a. If life were a video game, coping skills would be the extra
       lives, special abilities, protective armor, and weapons
       earned on each level.
    b. If life were a movie, coping skills would include the uplifting soundtrack, the feel-good
       scene that makes it worth watching, and the main character's refusal to give up in the
       face of impossible odds.
    c. Coping skills are methods we use to deal with life's challenges.
    d. Both A and B are right. C too.

2. Why devote time to coping skills? Choose more than one.

    a. We all need coping skills.
    b. Coping skills get you brownie points with the opposite sex.
    c. No matter how amazing and wise you are, there's always more to learn.
    d. Yeah, yeah, A and C are right.
    e. We're not sure about B.

3. Imagine that, prior to birth, you were granted one coping skill and one uplifting soundtrack to
   get through life. Which of the following would you choose?

    a. Rose-colored glasses with the soundtrack to *Amadeus* playing in the background.
    b. Karate with the *Karate Kid* soundtrack playing in the background.
    c. Tail-wagging abilities with the theme song from *Scooby Doo*.
    d. The ability to shape-shift accompanied by the soundtrack from *Avatar*.
    e. You haven't heard of any of these movies, and your favorite coping skill and soundtrack
       combination is no one's business.

4. True or False? "I don't need coping skills."

    a. If you chose true → Please turn to Day 10,876, "Why I need coping skills."
    b. If you chose false → What a relief. We don't want to write 10,876 worksheets. Please
       continue onto the next question.

5. You encounter a nasty cashier at the supermarket. How do you deal with your frustration?

    a. You feel overwhelmed and run away, accidently leaving your wallet at the supermarket.
    b. Say nothing and be upset about the situation all day. She ruined your life.
    c. Yell at the cashier, being as offensive as you can. You get thrown out.
    d. Step back, center yourself, and choose to not take it personally.

6. You're still in the supermarket, and the nasty cashier is still nasty. How else can you deal with frustration? (Choose more than one option.)

    a. Drop down and do 10 push-ups.
    b. Step outside the supermarket and call a friend for support.
    c. Talk to the cashier or their supervisor about the issue.
    d. Make up a horrible lie about the supermarket, forcing them to close. Eventually the lie is discovered, and you're banned from all local stores.

ANSWERS

1. (D) (all of the above) is right. Coping skills are about coping, resilience, and learning to soar.
2. All of the above except (B), although some say healthy coping skills are extremely sexy.
3. All answers are fine. But if your coping skills involve tail-wagging and *Scooby Doo*… you're extra cool. Woof.
4. The correct answer is (B), false. We *all* need coping skills.
5. Hopefully you chose (D). You calm yourself down so you can be more objective. In this case, you decide the cashier isn't worth your time. The other options all have negative consequences.
6. The right answers are (B) and (C). Reaching out for help or trying to actively fix the situation are fair approaches. (A) would be challenging to do inside the store, and (D) is a dishonest, unhealthy coping skill with negative consequences.

TIPS FOR COPING SKILLS

To further hit you over the head with coping skills, here are a few pointers:

1. **One skill doesn't fix all.** Different skills are suited for different types of problems.

    • If you are sitting in a field with an angry bull running toward you → do NOT journal.
    • If you've had a bad day at work → do NOT run, jump over a giant rock, dart to the left, dart to the right, book it to the fence, and hurl yourself over (unless absolutely necessary).

The trick is to collect coping skills like trophies. The more, the better.

2. **Avoid *bad* coping skills.** A skill is bad when it makes the problem worse. Examples include refusing to accept help or threatening violence to get your way. On the next page, you'll find a list of (mostly) negative coping skills. Circle the skills that are *healthy*.

EXAMPLES OF HEALTHY AND UNHEALTHY COPING SKILLS

Which of the following are examples of healthy coping skills? Circle all that apply.

a. Read an Outside-the-Box Recovery Workbook	b. Do anything in excess, like overeating, gambling, speeding, spending, or drugs
c. Refuse to communicate	d. Study for an upcoming exam
e. Watch *Scooby Doo* reruns to get yourself to smile	f. Focus only on the negative and exclude the positive
g. Eat a whole cake or two in one sitting	h. Help someone in the supermarket
i. Rely on someone else to make you happy	j. Do something useful or fun
k. Smoke a cigarette	l. Be controlling
m. Listen to heavy metal music	n. Let others take advantage of you
o. Start a movement to save a country from desolation	p. Lie or be misleading, or guilt others into doing things
q. Intimidate others on purpose	r. Hug a puppy when stressed.

ANSWERS

Most people would agree (D, E, H, J, and R) are healthy coping skills. (A) is helpful, we hope. (M) can be correct if heavy metal helps you stay clean. (O) is probably a good skill though not recommended during early recovery—save that for later. Yes, (K) is unhealthy!

A SURVIVAL STRATEGY LIST

You'll find 14 coping skills at the bottom of this page. Can you find them all in the puzzle?

■ ■

COPING SKILLS

```
G  I  M  A  G  I  N  E  T  R  I  U  M  P  H  I  N  G
B  E  M  I  N  D  F  U  L  Y  H  F  E  C  E  R  G  K
E  D  F  B  I  U  X  A  S  F  V  H  N  F  L  U  Y  D
T  W  A  E  V  L  O  S  M  E  L  B  O  R  P  U  A  C
H  A  S  K  F  O  R  H  E  L  P  O  R  H  S  D  V  C
A  R  O  M  A  T  H  E  R  A  P  Y  G  E  O  O  R  H
N  T  E  D  V  C  X  X  S  A  F  H  H  G  M  C  D  X
K  O  R  H  O  R  H  E  O  S  M  U  D  W  E  O  S  M
F  O  R  G  I  V  E  R  R  F  M  O  S  M  B  R  T  P
U  S  K  F  O  R  H  C  G  O  D  V  C  U  O  Y  R  A
L  D  V  C  A  F  T  I  R  C  H  K  U  K  D  A  V  D
M  O  S  M  B  M  O  S  H  O  R  H  E  O  Y  D  F  G
A  S  F  V  H  N  A  E  R  F  M  O  S  M  B  R  T  P
R  T  C  A  R  T  S  I  D  A  E  T  A  T  I  D  E  M
N  R  E  L  A  X  M  U  S  C  L  E  S  T  W  F  D  V
```

Ask for help	Distract	Imagine triumphing	Relax muscles
Aromatherapy	Exercise	Meditate	Use humor
Be mindful	Forgive	Pray	
Be thankful	Help somebody	Problem-solve	

■ ■

The answers are on page 141.

REFLECTION

Think of a personal situation or problem where a coping skill might be useful. Describe the issue, then come up with two good and two bad ways to deal with it.

For example:

You're at work. Four of your colleagues are off enjoying the beach, leaving you to run an important meeting. It starts in five minutes, and *you can't find your notes*! You're in a panic. Which coping skills might be helpful? Which would mess up your week? Here are some ideas, two good and two bad.

(a) Take comfortable belly-breathing breaths until you're calm. When you're ready, look for your notes. If you can't find them, ask someone else to run the meeting. GOOD

(b) Relax your shoulders, sit down, and calmly write out what you plan to talk about. GOOD

(c) Throw your stapler and accidently kill the office plant. BAD

(d) Drink lots of coffee and wing it, shaking and racing and all! BAD

Your turn! Describe an issue here, then list two good and two bad skills.

The take-home message: Coping skills are survival strategies that help people deal with painful situations and get through problems. Many of the upcoming worksheets present specific skills. Give each one a couple tries before moving onto the next one. Keep an eye out for skills that might be useful for you.

DAY 12. ACCEPTING EMOTIONS

PURPOSE OF THIS WORKSHEET:

- To explore and better understand emotions

1. CAPTURING FEELINGS ON PAPER

Think of a time when you felt bad. Were you worried, fearful, sad, angry, hurt, or something different? Imagine that feeling standing in front of you -- literally. What would it look like? Grab a pen or colored pencils and draw the feeling in the area below.

What, don't feel like drawing? Do it anyway!

When you're finished, add labels to describe what you drew. Pay attention to detail: Is the feeling an object or living creature? Does it move? Does it think? Is it childish or ancient? Does it know what it is? Make sure to include these details in your labels.

2. WHEN AN EMOTION SPEAKS TO YOU

Here you are standing face to face with a feeling. Suddenly it does the oddest thing: it speaks.
What does it say? Use the space below to write its words.

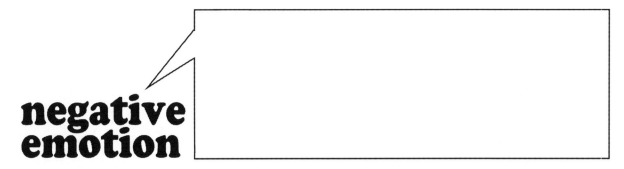

Imagine now that the emotion apologizes. "I never meant to hurt you, I'm sorry. Knowing that, can you accept me?" How would you respond? Write your answer in the box below.

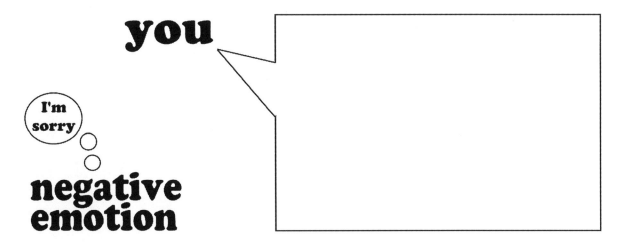

REFLECTION

What did your feeling look like? Did anything about your drawing surprise you?

How did your emotion and you relate? Compassionate strangers, warriors in combat, or something in between?

You'd think drawing and talking with a feeling wouldn't be all that productive, but looking at something from a distance and engaging with it lessens its hold on you. It's a great way to better understand difficult emotion. Thanks for participating!

DAY 13. MINDFULNESS

PURPOSE OF THIS WORKSHEET:

- To soothe painful emotion
- To get more out of good experiences

MINDFULNESS

Mindfulness is a way to seize the NOW. It anchors you in a safe place during life's difficult moments. It helps you maintain control in bad situations.

Mindfulness is also linked to greater peace and happiness. It's the difference between seeing a sunset of a thousand colors versus a boring glance at the sky.

This handout focuses on mindful listening. Read the instructions below, then use the next two pages to complete the exercise.

INSTRUCTIONS:

1. Take note of how you're feeling. Angry, happy, bored, overwhelmed? Jot it down at the top of the first page.

2. When you're ready, focus on *listening*. As you do, use the space on the next page to write about what you hear.

   - Listen to what surrounds you. Pay attention to each sound, noticing its volume, speed, location, intensity, and whatever else comes to mind.
   - If it's a mixture of noises, focus on one sound at a time.
   - If someone is speaking, listen to their voice, not their words. Are they speaking quickly or slowly? Do they take long pauses?
   - Don't judge the noise. Just take note.

3. Make sure to fill both pages with your observations. If everything is too quiet, imagine sounds that you like… the voice of somebody you care about, a favorite song, the rush of the ocean, etc.

4. When you're finished, take note again of how you're feeling. Record it at the end of the exercise.

LISTENING MINDFULNESS

1. Before you start: How do you feel? _____

2. Now listen. Pay attention to one sound at a time, listening to volume, speed, pauses, changes, type of sound, and anything else you notice. Use the space below and the next page to describe what you hear.

LISTENING MINDFULNESS
(CONTINUED)

3. When finished, check in with yourself again. How do you feel? _____

REFLECTION

How would mindful listening help when you're sad or angry?

How would mindful listening help at a concert?

What did you get out of this exercise? What can you do to make it more effective?

You can repeat this exercise as often as you'd like. Some people do it every day. Just find a piece of paper and record what you hear – or listen without writing. It's a powerful tool you can use anywhere and anytime, and the more you practice, the more it helps when you need it.

DAY 14. GRATITUDE

PURPOSE OF THIS HANDOUT:

- To find peace through gratitude
- To remember all the good things in your life

GRATITUDE.

A "gratitude list" is a list of things you appreciate. Creating this list helps you calm painful emotion, appreciate good experiences, and increase well-being. It's associated with greater *happiness*. What are you thankful for? Please go to the next page and start your list.

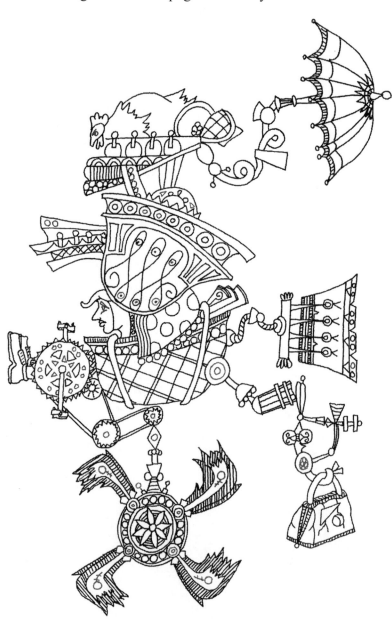

He was happy with his latest invention, the ACME GRATITUDE FLYING MACHINE 342.

It was fitted with everything he loved in life: his favorite umbrella, bag, shoes, and pet chicken, Gertrude. He had it all, and life was good – until he realized he'd forgotten his favorite landing gear at home.

GRATItude List

Please use the space below to make a list of stuff you appreciate. Repeat daily.

_____   _____

_____   _____

_____   _____

_____   _____

_____   _____

_____   _____

_____   _____

_____   _____

_____   _____

_____   _____

_____   _____

_____   _____

_____   _____

_____   _____

FIND WORDS.

How many words can you find in the expression, "GRATITUDE LIST?" Thanks. See page 141 for the answers. You receive extra credit for keeping it clean.

_____

_____

_____

_____

_____

_____

_____

_____

_____

REFLECTION

Look at your list. Is it short or long? Sometimes stress, depression, worry, anger, and other painful emotions can make it hard to think of things we appreciate. If that sounds familiar, review the following questions and add more answers to your gratitude list.

- What do you like best about nature? History? Technology? Mankind?
- Are there obstacles you're glad to have put behind you?
- What do you look forward to in the future? Which dreams give you hope?
- Is there a recent event that you enjoyed or felt especially thankful for?
- What made you laugh or smile today?

Homework, argh: Tonight, before you go to bed, think of five good things that happened during the day. Take time to do this every night.

Oh, by the way, did you remember to put *yourself* on the list?

DAY 15. JOURNALING

PURPOSE OF THIS WORKSHEET:

- To soothe painful emotion and/or find meaning through journaling

WHY JOURNAL?

Journaling gets us through dark times; it's a place to rest your head when the world seems a crazy place. It also helps organize this crazy place into something manageable. But, more than anything, it offers hope: Journaling is like an old friend, always curious to hear your story.

Journaling is good for many things:

Cheering yourself up	Calming yourself down	Solving problems
Writing fiction and poetry	Processing memories	Understanding yourself better
Finding inspiration	Recording your day	Embracing spirituality
Accessing your true self	Planning the future	Remembering dreams

All you need is a pen and paper. And today we supply the paper.

INSTRUCTIONS

1. It's simple: Write.
2. Write some more
3. So you're not ready to write? No problem, we've got you covered. Go to the next page and review our Journaling FAQ.

YOUR QUESTIONS

Do I have to do this worksheet? Yes, at least this once.

I can't spell. I can't do grammar. My handwriting is scary. My brain cramps every time I think about journaling. My ideas are scandalous. I can't do it. Help. Help. Do I have to? Relax your brain, be gentle with yourself, and don't write about anything that makes you uncomfortable. You can also destroy the document after you finish. But do journal today please. Give it a try.

How much should I write? We recommend a couple pages. That's enough to open your mind and get some real stuff on paper.

What should I write? Anything. So you want to discuss the meaning of life? Great! Want to explore your relationship with a pair of shoes you saw at the shops? Go ahead! Anything is game, as long as you write write write. If you don't know what to write, just jot down anything that comes to mind. Thoughts? Sensations? To-do list? What you're worried about? It all counts.

What if I STILL don't know what to write? Then write about not knowing what to write.

> *"What do I write? Nothing, something, oh dear, nothing, no no nothing on my mind,*
> *so I'm just going to write random words... neighbors, shoes, crazy worksheets..."*

The trick is to keep your pen moving. Don't worry about content; it'll come on its own. Just fill the empty page with words.

What if I get tired of writing about not knowing what to write? If you absolutely must have a writing prompt, here are some journaling ideas.

- If you're feeling bad, use the paper to complain about everything, then rewrite it all using exaggerated, positive words.

  "I feel like everyone hates me" → *"I feel mankind embracing my very existence..."*

- Pick something in view and describe it, taking note of every detail, from color and shadow and texture to movement and sound. For extra credit, include a sketch.
- Think about recovery. How has it changed the way you feel and think about life?
- Make a list of your problems. Choose one and write about it. How does it affect you, and what can you do to improve the situation?
- Describe your first childhood memory.

Now go to the next page and give it a try.

REFLECTION

What did you get out of your journaling experience?

What did you write about? Was it a helpful topic?

What surprised you? What did you learn or discover?

Some of the greatest minds became great by recording their reflections on paper. It's that powerful. Whether you type your ideas into your computer, record your voice, make a video, write everything by hand, or use smoke signals to get the message across, use this resource to improve your greatness!

TAKE A BREAK, THE MAZE OF HOPE

Apart from all the hopes, can you find your way through this maze? See the answer on p142.

DAY 16. RECOGNIZING PROBLEM THOUGHTS

PURPOSE OF THIS WORKSHEET:

- To recognize thoughts that bring you down

WHAT ARE PROBLEM THOUGHTS?

Problem thoughts are negative, unhealthy, dead-end thoughts that make you feel bad and make relapse more likely. Often, they're based on false information. Problem thoughts lead to bad outcomes. Healthy thoughts are the opposite. They are realistic, feel good, and make a positive outcome possible.

IDENTIFYING A PROBLEM THOUGHT

You have a thought. Whatever it is, it's bothering you. How can you tell if it's a problem thought? Ask yourself the following questions.

→ **Is the thought opinion or fact?** A fact isn't a problem thought. For example, "Cats are 4-legged devils" is an opinion. "Cats are mammals" is a fact.

→ **How does it make you feel?** A problem thought typically spoils your mood or makes you want to do something you shouldn't. If you think, "I'm a useless person. Everything I do is wrong," you'll probably feel incompetent.

→ **Does the thought lead you to a good place?** Problem thoughts are usually dead-ends. They have negative outcomes. For example, if you think, "I can't stop using, it's impossible," the outcome is a poor one.

→ **Does the thought ignore information?** Your perspective is problematic if you don't look at the whole picture. For example, "All teenagers are nasty" ignores the fact that many teenagers aren't.

Problem thoughts go against well-being. In the end they lower your spirits and point you in the wrong direction. You'll find sixteen thoughts below. Which ones are problematic?

THOUGHT LIST
Circle all problem thoughts.

a. If you hug a cat, it starts purring. That's called cat therapy, ha ha. Just joking.

b. You are a faceless imp with an ugly mother. It's your fault I did that!

c. I'll never be able to do this. It's overwhelming, and I'm just too stupid.

d. I've been using so long, I'll never quit. It's too late for me.

e. I was offensive and I regret it, but I can still apologize and try to make things ok.

f. He didn't call me today. That means he doesn't love me. I'm bad at relationships.

g. I've been sober for six months now. It's hard but getting easier.

h. There's a lot of tragedy in the world but also a lot of people overcoming it.

i. It's hopeless. Alcohol has ruined my life. There's no fixing things.

j. I can drink in moderation. This time it'll be different, I promise.

k. My boss was looking at me funny, but that doesn't mean she's mad at me.

l. I'm good with cats. I can fix just about any cat problem.

m. I'm so upset that the only way to calm myself is popping a pill.

n. My computer crashed. It's horrible, but I have this friend who might help.

o. It takes time for me to trust people. I care about him, but I'm still working on trust.

p. Mankind is evil. All you have to do is watch the news.

ANSWERS

Dividing healthy from unhealthy can be difficult. Let's take the list one by one.

Which are unhealthy? (B) is a problem; name-calling and blaming others for something you did are rarely healthy. (C&D) are problematic because they make you feel incompetent and lead to a negative outcome; it would be healthier to think, "This is hard, but I can try." Thoughts like (F) are bad for relationships; you might feel unloved, but his reason for not calling might be something completely different. (I) is problematic, in that it feels bad and often leads to relapse; it's never too late to try to fix things. The ability to drink in moderation (J) and using when upset (M) are problematic in that they hurt the chances of recovery. Finally, (P) is a problem thought: focusing only on the bad and ignoring the good is a miserable approach to life. Notice that many of these opinions are relapse-justifying.

The others thoughts are healthy. Some are random opinions, like (A) and (L) about cats. They can be helpful, if you like cats. Others, like (E, G, H, K, N, and O) recognize a problem but understand it's still possible to have a good outcome.

2. WHAT'S ON YOUR MIND?

Your turn. Think of a difficult task, like a project or problem you're struggling with. Fill in the box below with worries, frustrations, and fears about the task. Be specific.

REFLECTION

How have you typically dealt with problem thoughts in the past?

It's common to have bothersome thoughts. Sometimes we're not even aware of them, but they ruin our day anyway. People often manage these "cognitions" by thinking about them obsessively without finding a solution. Others ignore them and feel worse. Still others take drugs to forget them, but the thoughts are still around when they return to reality.

In the next worksheet, we'll work at changing problem thoughts.

DAY 17. CHANGING PROBLEM THOUGHTS

PURPOSE OF THIS WORKSHEET:

- To use a magic ball to change negative thoughts into healthy ones
- To realize there is no magic ball, but you can improve your thinking anyway

1. AH...PROBLEM THOUGHTS

We're not made to feel bad. When we do, it's usually caused by problem thoughts. How can you tell if a thought is problematic? Focus on how it affects you. If it makes you feel trapped or negative or gives you the urge to do something you shouldn't, it's likely on the problem side.

Healthy thoughts promote well-being. They're realistic, taking both positive and negative into consideration, and in the end lift your mood and point you in the right direction.

FINDING THAT THOUGHT

How do you deal with problem thoughts? First, you have to find them.

Think of a tough situation you're facing, a problem you feel you can't solve. What are your doubts about the situation? What kinds of negative or problem thoughts come up? List as many as you can here. (This is a take off from Worksheet 16).

Amidst the thoughts you described above, circle the one that bothers you the most.

MANAGING PROBLEM THOUGHTS

The trick to handling painful thoughts is to find a different angle or perspective. You need to rework the thought into something more reality-based, recovery-promoting, and healthier. Imagine you have two people inside you. One is called Worry, and the other, Wisdom.

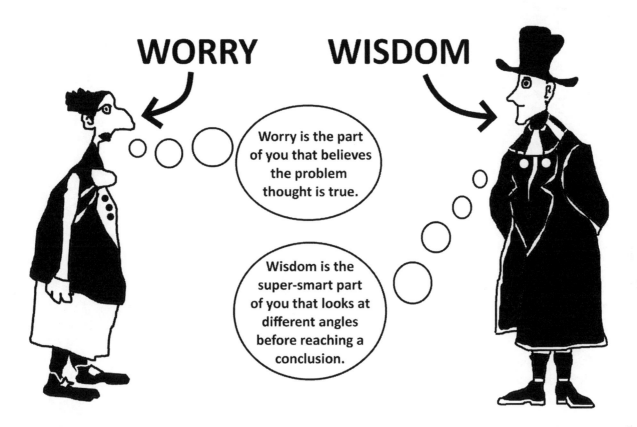

WORRY   **WISDOM**

Worry is the part of you that believes the problem thought is true.

Wisdom is the super-smart part of you that looks at different angles before reaching a conclusion.

WORRY SPEAKS AND WISDOM ANSWERS

There's a room inside your head (humor us, please) with a space big enough to furnish a small table and two chairs. The table is covered with a white cloth, and there are words embroidered across it: *Why worry? Be wise.*

Enter Worry and Wisdom. Each takes a seat. Worry is uncomfortable, and its eyes dart left and right. It's here to defend the problem thought. Wisdom floats above the chair, a picture of calm. It's here to examine and rewrite the problem thought.

Choose one negative thought from your list and complete the boxes on the next page.

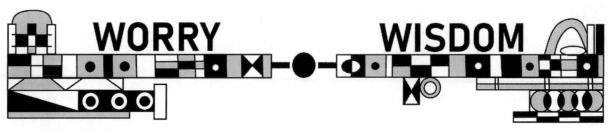

To rewrite a problem thought, complete the boxes below and on the next page.

1. Worry speaks. Write the problem thought here.	**2. Wisdom answers.** Wisdom understands Worry's point of view. What evidence is there that Worry is right?
	Wisdom sees where Worry is mistaken. What evidence is there that Worry is wrong? Here are some ideas to consider: • Are there other ways to look at the problem? • Is Worry looking only at the negative and forgetting the positive? • What would a wise friend say about Worry's thought? (Continued on the next page.)

3. The thought is rewritten. Wisdom thinks a good while before making a final speech. Complete the sentence: "Worry's point of view might seem true, but a healthier way to look at it is…"

STUMPED? HERE ARE SOME EXAMPLES

Problem Thought: This is Worry's belief, a dead-end thought that makes him feel bad or want to do something unhealthy.	**Healthy Thought:** Worry's point of view might seem true, but a healthier way to look at it is…
My boss was looking at me funny. That means I'm going to lose my job →	Chances are the look had nothing to do with me. Besides, I do good work. It's unlikely I'll get fired.
I can drink in moderation. This time it'll be different, I promise. →	I've tried drinking in moderation and always run into problems. The thought doesn't mean I need to give into it. I can hold onto recovery.

REFLECTION

How did rewriting the thought change your feelings?

How did rewriting the thought change your approach to the problem?

Rewriting a negative thought usually brings about a sense of relief or improved decision-making. If you don't feel better after this exercise, share your thoughts with someone you trust and ask for feedback.

TAKE A BREAK, SHE SAID NO

Consuela was good at saying NO. Can you find the 12 differences between these two pictures? The answers are on page 143.

DAY 18. REPLACING DRUGS WITH THE GOOD STUFF

PURPOSE OF THIS WORKSHEET:

- To help you replace drugs with fun stuff
- To remember that, in addition to fun, life is filled with "good stuff" to replace drugs

DON'T THINK ABOUT DRUGS 1

Stop -- don't think about drugs or alcohol. Read the following sentences without imagining anything related to addicting substances.

➔ 92000 people died from drug-related overdose in 2020, more than half from synthetic opioids.

➔ When used long term, alcohol can cause vitamin deficiencies, anemia, problems walking, loss of sensation in legs, heart failure, bleeding intestines, memory and thinking problems, stroke, cirrhosis & liver failure, liver cancer, six other types of cancer, and much more.

DON'T THINK ABOUT DRUGS 2.

Alright, now read the following without thinking of drugs…this time filling in the blanks with the words found on the right.

> Fill in the blanks using the words below. Pick as many as you want.
>
> *My mother-in-law*
>
> *My right leg*
>
> *Freddy Kruger*
>
> *Cinderella*
>
> *My psychiatrist*

➔ ~~Cocaine~~ _____ is sometimes laced with the opioid Fentanyl and can cause accidental overdose and death.

➔ ~~Methamphetamine~~ _____ can cause permanent brain damage, making the user dependent on others for basic care.

➔ Mixing ~~alcohol~~ _____ and benzodiazepines like ~~Klonopin~~_____ can be deadly.

WHERE ARE WE GOING WITH THIS?

How hard was it to NOT think about drugs and alcohol? It seemed impossible with the first sentences, right? Tell me to avoid thinking about something, and I think about it more! But, in the second set, we replaced the drugs with something else. That made it easier to ignore them.

As the title suggests, this worksheet is about replacing chemicals with the good stuff… we'll start with the fun stuff

Fun isn't always easy. It can be tough to enjoy life, especially in early recovery, when your brain is still healing. If you can't *feel* fun, go through the motions until it kicks in. Sometimes all it takes is that first step.

THE FUN LIST

HOW DO YOU REPLACE DRUGS? START WITH THE FUN STUFF!

Make a list of stuff you can do instead of thinking about or using drugs. This should be things you like or would like to do. Need more ideas? Check out ours below.

Instructions: Are you looking for something fun, goofy, distracting, or a little odd? Review the list below and circle the options that interest you. Note that most of the "apps" are for smartphones – explore at your own risk!

Learn how to read auras	Change your cat's looks with the app, "Cat paint"
Eat toast with butter	Become sentient toast using app, "I am bread"
Talk to your pet	Listen to your pet talk
Eat the whole world using the app "Hole.io"	Visit "Second Life" on your computer
Tour a virtual zoo	Watch a video of a fainting goat on YouTube
Ride a motorcycle	Go surfing
Attend a 12-Step meeting	Wear your sunglasses at night
Go on a date to the airport	Convince somebody you're from the future
Make a hilarious, personal photo calendar	Make a hilarious photo calendar for someone else
Shave virtually using the app, "iShaver Pro"	Practice a new accent
Learn to roller-skate	Learn how to twirl roller-skating
Virtually smash stuff with app, "Crack & break it"	Don't smash stuff in real life
Color in a coloring book	Write a fiction piece about a duck
Cuddle with someone or something	Get a massage
Virtually milk a cow with app, "Milk the cow"	Learn how to milk a real cow
Use a pirate's voice with the app, "Carr Matey"	Visit a toy store and play with everything
Train a parrot to talk	Teach a parrot to speak Korean
Press flowers and leaves in a notebook	Visit an online aquarium
Search your name online	Try to erase your online identity
Sharpen a carrot as much as possible	Listen to music that brings back healthy memories
Go to the opera	Sing a mean opera in the shower
Plant an indoor vegetable, like sweet potato	Go to the store and buy yourself some flowers
See like a goat using the app, "Goat simulator"	Do origami and make something out of paper
Meditate and reach nirvana	Eat a bowl of ice cream… or broccoli
Visit kimrosenthalmd.com for more fun stuff	Read an *Outside-the-Box Recovery Workbook*

PART OF RECOVERY IS SETTING UP A SOBER IDENTITY, SOMETHING YOU LOVE.

There's more than fun. Over time you'll want to replace drugs with other stuff, like activities that give you a sense of achievement (see Day 19), growth, reflection/meaning, spirituality, friendship, health, etc. Sometimes this feels overwhelming and impossible. To belabor the point that **anything is possible**, go to the Reflection on the next page and solve the code.

REPLACING DRUGS WITH THE GOOD STUFF

"Nobody stays **RECOVERED** unless the life they have created is more **REWARDING** and **SATISFYING** than the one they leave behind."
-ANNE FLETCHER

REFLECTION

Recovery is about creating a life you love. How can you make your life more rewarding and satisfying? Answer the question in the space below.

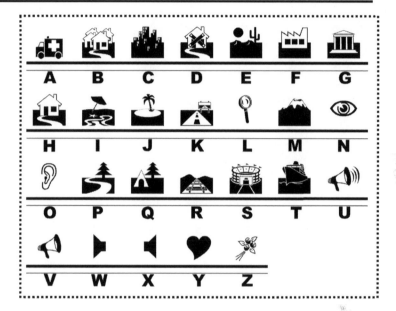

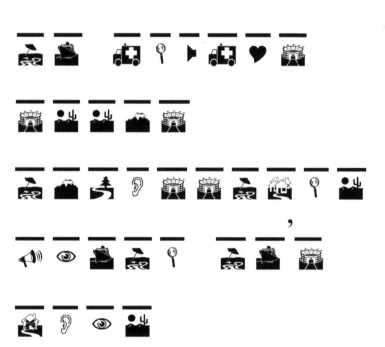

Next, using the legend at top-right, can you decode this quotation by Nelson Mandela? The answer is on page 144.

DAY 19. NEEDS & WANTS: MAKING A SCHEDULE

PURPOSE OF THIS WORKSHEET:

- To learn the importance of keeping yourself busy
- To help you create a daily schedule

PHONE IN CONTROL. Imagine your phone runs your schedule, not you. "Ding ding, time to watch boring stuff on TV." "Ding ding, time to go spy on your ex-boyfriend." "Ding ding, time to sit for three hours and do nothing." You always do what it says. "Ding ding, you're still bored. Time to visit that nasty neighbor, you know the one who keeps stealing your shoes." You'll find two rounds of questions below.

ROUND ONE

1. What happens if YOU don't control your schedule? Choose more than one.

   (a) Chances are somebody or something else does
   (b) You're more likely to get yourself into trouble
   (c) It's possible you're in jail, prison, or a hospital

2. If you don't control your free time, who does? Choose more than one.

   (a) If you're in early recovery, drugs might be in charge by default.
   (b) Yeah, drugs. Your day is filled with cravings, triggers, and drug thoughts.
   (c) You're in control – except you're not giving yourself a schedule, so → not really you.

3. Why organize a schedule? Choose more than one.

   (a) Too much free time raises the risk of relapse
   (b) Completing the stuff on your schedule gives you purpose
   (c) Well, if you want to become a politician, it can help you avoid scandal.
   (d) It helps you get things done

4. Which of the following is the best schedule?

   (a) Wake up. Watch sunrise. 12-Step meeting. Doctor's appointment. Meet with girlfriend # 1. Window shop downtown. Meet with girlfriend #2 for more window shopping. Go see accountant. Meet with girlfriend #3. Break up. Go to movies with girlfriend #4. Stop by pet store. Steal a puppy. Meet with girlfriend #23. Return stolen puppy. Bed.
   (b) Wake up. Video games. Ice cream. Wander about the park. Drift down the street without focus. More ice cream. Watch TV. Bed.
   (c) Wake up. Do 10 jumping jacks. Video games. Doctor's appointment. Grocery shopping. Meeting. Watch TV. Call sponsor. Eat ice cream. Bed.

ANSWERS TO ROUND ONE

1. All options are correct. If you're incarcerated or hospitalized, focus on what you can control – your down time.
2. All are true.
3. (A), (B), and (D) are right. (C) we're not sure about; even politicians benefit from schedules, but a schedule doesn't avoid scandal.
4. (C) is the right answer. Why? (A) is jam-packed with activities, but too many! The pace is unreasonable, there's no time to relax, and having that many girlfriends is dangerous. And no one should steal puppies. (B) Why is B wrong? It includes a list of fun activities, but no "NEED" tasks. What does that mean? Keep reading…

When making a schedule, it's important to include both "WANT" and "NEED" tasks. Basically, WANT = FUN and NEED = ACHIEVEMENT. The picture below shows the difference.

Want

A "want" is something fun, like dancing to your favorite song

Examples of "wants"

Eating ice cream
Cuddling with a cat
Hanging out with friends
Smelling a flower
Watching a movie
Buying a funny-looking fish
Kissing someone

Need

A "need" helps you achieve, like attending Weight Watchers

Examples of "needs"

Paying bills
Cleaning the house
Making an important phone call
Going to a doctor's appointment
Studying for an exam
Doing 20 jumping jacks
Buying laundry detergent

ROUND TWO

We've talked about schedules a lot so far, but there's more. Choose true or false.

1. _____ Schedules are only for people who are employed or in school.

2. _____ A schedule must keep you busy all the time.

3. _____ It's important to go to sleep and wake up at the same time every day.

4. _____ There isn't time to do everything. You have to prioritize.

5. _____ Schedules are society's way of controlling us.

6. _____ Artists and musicians are less productive if they have a schedule.

7. _____ The worksheet wants to take over your brain with a schedule.

ANSWERS TO ROUND TWO

1. False. Schedules can help anyone, regardless of their employment or academic status.

2. False. An overly busy schedule, one that leaves you no downtime or enjoyment, is a bad idea. That kind of schedule tends to burn a person out. It's to be avoided, if possible.

3. True. The inner clock tends to create stability and wellness when a person schedules sleep at the same time every day.

4. True. Your to-do list might be bigger than you, but it's very hard to do it all in one day. The trick is to prioritize; that means choosing what's most important first.

5. False. No to society! You're in control if you handle your own time.

6. False. Surprising but this is false. An artist can increase productivity by keeping a schedule!

7. True. Just kidding, this is false. It's tempting, though.

TIPS FOR SCHEDULING

On the next page, you're going to create a schedule. To help you prepare, consider the following questions and answers.

How do I keep a schedule if I have no money? Ah, a money issue, common in early recovery. Luckily there are plenty of low-cost or free things to do. Here are some ideas. Check those that you're already doing or would like to do.

☐ Go through my books	☐ Call my sponsor	☐ Go to a meeting
☐ Watch old family videos	☐ Go window-shopping	☐ Sketch a flower
☐ Help someone	☐ Visit the library	☐ Plant an orange seed
☐ Organize my photos	☐ Go hiking or for a walk	☐ Doodle
☐ Make an origami box	☐ Collect leaves	☐ Play on a swing
☐ Look for a job	☐ Apply for a scholarship	☐ Call old friends
☐ Attend free events	☐ Take a free class	☐ Sew up holes in clothing
☐ Study a new language	☐ Practice math	☐ Dress up something crazy

What do I do if I have no house, phone, transportation, books, or money? You're in a tough situation, my friend, but there are always things you can do. If you need help, go to a local shelter or somewhere safe. Ask for a list of resources. Alternative options might be a 12-Step meeting, church, public mental health clinic, or emergency room. You can also call the homeless 2-1-1 hotline or search "help for homelessness" online. Above all, add *hope* to your schedule. You'll get past this.

I'm in prison. How do I make a schedule if I don't control my own time? You have control over your thoughts and sense of humor, and you have a pinch of free time. Not much, but take advantage of it. Make sure to exercise, journal, meditate, read, watch movies, play cards, reach out to family and friends, research stuff that interests you, learn a new skill, get an education, and honor true friendship when you see it. Volunteer to help others. Schedule time for meetings and support groups. Once ready, consider leadership roles and counseling.

I'm stuck in the hospital... no pens, no access to internet, nothing to study, and no way am I doing math here. What can I do? Hospitals take away a lot of freedoms, but they also give you plenty of downtime. Consider using that time to exercise, stretch, color, do puzzles, meditate, relax your muscles, meet with providers and staff when needed, and plan your discharge. The good thing about inpatient care is that it's rarely permanent.

My mother-in-law won't let me do anything... Really? Now that's a problem. We suggest you run. Now. Then do something.

HOW TO MAKE A SCHEDULE:

1. **To-Do List.** What would you like to do tomorrow? Make a list of *everything* that's on your mind, including wants (fun) and needs (achievement).

2. **Prioritize.** Next, narrow down your list. Out of the activities above, circle "needs" that are required or most urgent. Circle a few "wants" you'd enjoy doing. Don't overdo it with too much!

3. **Schedule**. Finally, go to the next page and start your schedule! Start with a time for each "need." Next, add your "wants." (You'll find a little example below)

Use this schedule to organize your day.

DAILY SCHEDULE

Use this space for notes

Date: _____

5AM

6AM

7AM

8AM

9AM

10AM

11AM

NOON

1PM

2PM

3PM

4PM

5PM

6PM

7PM

8PM

9PM

10PM

11PM

REFLECTION

When will you do the stuff in your schedule?

    (a) Next year
    (b) Someday
    (c) Tomorrow
    (d) Yesterday

The right answer is (C). It's tomorrow's schedule, so it makes sense to start tomorrow. How many activities should you schedule every day? Choose more than one.

    (a) If you're new to recovery and have nothing to do, four or five is fine
    (b) If you're used to keeping a schedule, you can plan more.
    (c) At least seven an hour
    (d) One 12-Step or support meeting/day is enough.

(A and B) are correct. (C) is for slave-drivers. (D) is questionable; there's too much free time. You need more than one event/day. Frankly, the number of activities/day will vary, depending on your preference. Some people do fine with four, others prefer ten.

So what can you do tomorrow morning to make it happen?

    (a) Ask someone to give you something to do
    (b) Look at the clock and start with the activity you scheduled
    (c) Nothing. All these activities are boring, ridiculous, or impossible
    (d) Lose your schedule.

Which did you choose? The best answer is (B). (C) is a poor answer; it's your job to impress yourself, to fill your schedule with joy and achievement, so keep your schedule interesting! If the tasks seem impossible, break them down into smaller steps. If you lose your schedule, make another one.

Between Days 18 and 19, we took on fun stuff and the importance of replacing addictive behavior with something worthwhile. We also introduced "needs" or "achievement tasks" and figured out how to put both wants and needs in a schedule. The next step? Do what's on your schedule! Thanks for reading. Come back tomorrow for more! (You did put us in your schedule, didn't you?")

TAKE A BREAK.   CONTACT WITH BELANG

IMAGINE THE FUTURE

The year is 3689. Belang is your grandson 28 times removed, and he just spent a day cleaning acid-flowers off the dome of his latest terraforming planet project. He's exhausted, but not enough to ignore this morning's discovery: he found a 1,500-year-old electronic document hidden in his files. It's a letter. In fact, it's a letter written to *him,* to Belang, from his ancestor. That ancestor is you.

Using the space below, write a letter to Belang. Imagine he's a real descendant and will truly receive this letter. What would you tell him? What message or advice would you send? If he could respond, what questions would you ask? And the big question: Do you tell him about your drug/alcohol abuse? Write your letter thoughtfully.

REFLECTION

Imagine you receive a letter from an ancestor who lived 1500 years ago. What would that be like? What would you NOT want to know?

DAY 20. HONESTY

PURPOSE OF THIS WORKSHEET:

- To work on personal growth
- To better understand honesty

1. YOUR THOUGHTS

"Trust takes years to build, seconds to break, and it can never be repaired." Do you agree with this quotation? Once lost, can trust be earned again? Why or why not?

Why is trust important, anyway?

2. TRUSTING A LAWYER

Here's a story: A. Turney was the best lawyer in town. She was passionate. She was trusted. She received a standing ovation everywhere she went. In fact, the US President had her number on speed dial. She was *that* awesome... until she relapsed.

Now the lawyer has been sober for five days.

She's quit, but life isn't perfect. While drinking, Turney drove dangerously, so her husband took away the car keys and won't give them back. At work, she wasn't on top of her game anymore, which caused major problems for one client. Eventually she had to stop working. And then last week, she was so drunk that her 9-year-old had to care for her all night.

1. Which of the following is true about alcoholic lawyers?

    a. Attorneys never have substance use disorders. This story is fake news.
    b. According to the Journal of Addiction Medicine Jan/Feb 2016, lawyers are almost twice as likely to be problem drinkers compared to non-lawyers.

2. Anyone can develop a drug problem. It touches all walks of life: nuns, children, politicians, and yes, attorneys. That makes (B) correct for #1. But Turney stopped drinking and wants to get back to life as normal. She's fixed, right? What happens next?

    a. Within 48 hours, everyone trusts her again. She is happy. Everyone is happy.
    b. Her husband and daughter are worried she'll drink, and they notice everything she does. The court wants her to get treatment before returning to work.

3. Things are far from normal. The right answer is (B). But the lawyer quit drinking – why doesn't anyone trust her?

    a. It's not her fault. Others just don't understand that she's cured and should be trusted.
    b. The lawyer needs to earn back trust. She's healing (not cured), and everyone exposed to her addiction needs to heal too. That takes time.

4. The unfortunate truth is that quitting doesn't equal "cured," making (B) the right option. Quitting is the first step in a long journey. How long will it take for Turney to get back trust? Choose more than one of the following options.

    a. Not too long. She doesn't have a DUI, still has her driver's license, still has a job, and that thing with her kid only happened once. Things aren't too bad.
    b. People should trust her immediately.
    c. It takes exactly two months.
    d. If they don't trust her after six months, there's something wrong with them.
    e. It happens little by little and can take years.
    f. She'll never get anyone to trust her ever again.
    g. There are some people who won't trust her again.
    h. She'll get trust back more quickly if she demands people to trust her.
    i. She'll get trust back more quickly if she shows she can be trusted.

Some people will never trust her again, but others will… little by little and only after a long period of time. We're talking months to years. That means (E) and (G) are correct. (I) is true too; people are more likely to trust her if she shows she's trustworthy. Demanding trust from others (H) doesn't work.

3. A WHOLE LOT OF TRUST

To emphasize the important of the word, we've created a TRUST word search. How many times can you find the word "trust" in the puzzle. The answer is on page 144.

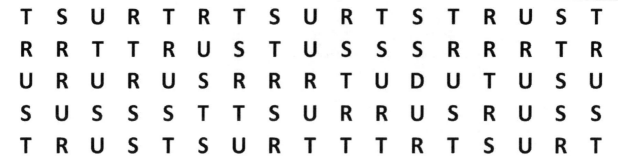

```
T  S  U  R  T  R  T  S  U  R  T  S  T  R  U  S  T
R  R  T  T  R  U  S  T  U  S  S  S  R  R  R  T  R
U  R  U  R  U  S  R  R  R  T  U  D  U  T  U  S  U
S  U  S  S  S  T  T  S  U  R  R  U  S  R  U  S  S
T  R  U  S  T  S  U  R  T  T  T  R  T  S  U  R  T
```

4. BUT HOW DO YOU EARN BACK TRUST?

Substance use disorders make us do things we regret, often towards other people. It takes time to heal those relationships. Not sure where to start? Check out these tips below.

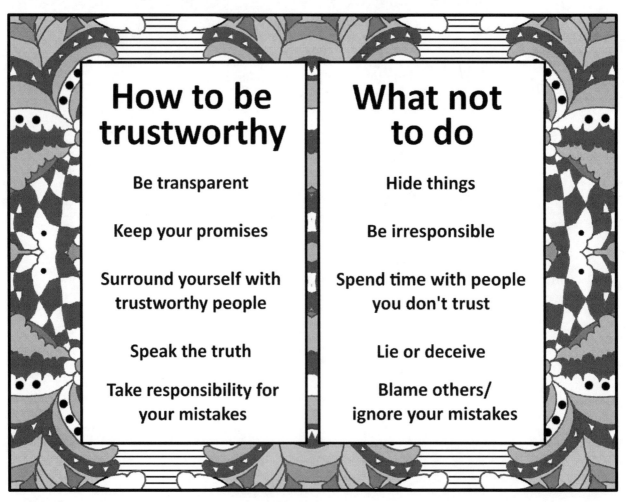

How to be trustworthy

Be transparent

Keep your promises

Surround yourself with trustworthy people

Speak the truth

Take responsibility for your mistakes

What not to do

Hide things

Be irresponsible

Spend time with people you don't trust

Lie or deceive

Blame others/ ignore your mistakes

In the picture above, the list on the left is where you put your money. But how can you tell if you're being honest? If in doubt, think about the people you trust and do what they're doing.

5. WHEN NO ONE TRUSTS YOU

Back to A. Turney's story: The lawyer has been clean 1 month now, but word of her alcohol problem is out. Most of her clients refuse to work with her. How can she best deal with the situation? Choose more than one of the following options.

a. The lawyer focuses on herself. She can be trustworthy, even if no one else believes it. She works to build *integrity*,* regardless of the opinions of others.
b. The lawyer invests her energy in the future. She finally gets permission to work again. Although she never gets her old clients back, in time she connects with new ones.
c. The lawyer recognizes that trust is earned back little by little. She focuses on the small successes and takes it one day at a time, appreciating those who do trust her.
d. The lawyer spends all her time telling her old clients she can be trusted.
e. The lawyer blames her old clients for messing up her career.

*You probably know this, but humor us: *Being reliable, responsible, and trustworthy is called integrity*. If you keep to your word… regardless of what others think… that is honorable, and that's what matters. Out of the options above, (A), (B), and (C) are the best answers.

REFLECTION

We're all trying to improve ourselves, and trust is vital to growth. What three things can you do to be more trustworthy? Using the space below, write a brief letter to the people in your life answering this question.

Dear family and friends:

Love

DAY 21. BEING A GOOD FRIEND

PURPOSE OF THIS WORKSHEET:

- Learn more about being a good friend
- To get lost in a jungle (ha ha)

THE JUNGLE STORY

This worksheet is about being a good friend. To better help you explore friendship, you'll find a series of boxes below.

Please read each box and answer all questions. Note the boxes aren't meant to be read in order. Follow directions!

---

1. START HERE. A friend and you are kidnapped. You wake up in a tropical jungle.

   Your friend is upset and frazzled. "Oooh, I don't like bugs or snakes or crocodiles or leeches or…" The list continues. What do you do? Choose 1A or 1B.

 1A. You interrupt immediately. "Pull it together. We have to find shelter before darkness comes. There's no time for such nonsense." Go to # 4.

 1B. You recognize your friend is freaking out, and telling them to stop won't help. You listen a moment before reassuring them that you'll both do everything in your power to survive. Go to # 4.

---

2. Noooo! Stop! You shouldn't be here. Please go back to #1 and follow the directions. Thanks.

   You're still here? Go, friend, go! Don't waste time here. Just don't.

3. EMPATHY. 6B was the better option. This question was about empathy, the ability to understand and feel for others. This is the "I get you" part of friendship. Describe a time when someone didn't care to understand you. How did you feel?

   Describe three ways you can show more empathy.

   Go to #9.

THE JUNGLE STORY (CONTINUED)

4. LISTENING. To be a good friend, you have to be a good listener, making option 1B a superior choice. Option 1A ignores your friend's worries. By listening, you realize they need reassurance, not tough love. Tough love would probably make your friend worse. Go to #7.

5. DEAD END. Option 5 is a dead end. There's no reason to be here. Please go back to #1 and avoid #5 completely.

6. Your friend turns pale. "I'm panicking. This is awful." How do you respond, 6A or 6B?

6A. "A panic attack, now? You can't be having those here, man. It's too dangerous." Go to # 3.

6B. "I understand it's scary. Sit and relax a moment. We'll start walking in five." Go to #3.

7. Describe a time when somebody wouldn't listen to what you had to say. How did it feel?

How can you be a better listener?

Go to #6.

8. Your friend and you follow the river until you reach a beach. You're both exhausted. It's getting late. Your friend agrees to gather branches for a shelter while you look for food. As the sun sets, you find a trail with a sign reading "Rescue, that way!" What do you do? Choose 8A or 8B.

8A. You ditch the food-hunting and follow the trail. There's no time to go get your friend. You'll come back. Go to #10

8B. You put the trail aside for now and look for food. You promised you'd bring back food, and that's what you do. Go to #10.

9. Your friend calms down. "Thanks for caring…I think we should camp here for the night. I'm too tired to keep moving." Your friend is insistent, but you disagree. It's important to start walking. There's no shelter here. Which of the options is the most respectful response? Choose 9A, 9B, or 9C on the next page.

BE KIND • BE A GOOD LISTENER • HAVE RESPECT
HAVE EMPATHY • KEEP PROMISES • BE KIND(AGAIN)

THE JUNGLE STORY (CONTINUED)

Read the scenario and choose 9A, 9B, or 9C.

9A. "If you want to stay, we'll stay." You don't want to upset your friend by disagreeing with them. Go to # 11.	9B. "You know what? I don't care what you're saying. At this point I'm going to knock you unconscious and carry you if I have to." The only respectful thing is to try to save their life. Go to #11.	9C. "I understand what you're saying, but I disagree. We really need to find water and shelter." They agree to walk slowly. Go to #11.

10. KEEP PROMISES. For friendship to work, you must be reliable. If you say you're going to do something, you should do it. 8A means you either abandon your friend or return without food. 8B is the better option. Go to #13.

11. RESPECT. Relationships need respect. You respect others by caring about their point of view as much as your own, by treating others well. 9C is the best option, since it shows respect for your needs as well as your friend's, plus a willingness to find a middle-of-the-road solution.

Describe a time when someone was disrespectful to you. How did it feel?

How can you be more respectful?

Go to #8.

12. You return to the beach with food and water from the river. Your friend has already built a shelter and started a fire. It's a safe night, and you wake up to find a sunrise.

The next day you're caught by a man-eating tribe, but your friend rescues you… only to have a volcano erupt nearby. Luckily your friend has a mirror, which they use to attract a ship. The ship almost sinks on the way to rescue, but in the end everything turns out okay.

Your friend and you make a grand movie about your adventure and make millions. You eventually figure out who kidnapped you, but that's another story. THE END.

13. Describe a time when someone broke their promise and let you down. How did you feel?

How can you be more reliable?

Go to #12.

**BE KIND • BE A GOOD LISTENER • HAVE RESPECT
HAVE EMPATHY • KEEP PROMISES • BE KIND(AGAIN)**

REFLECTION

The story described various characteristics of a good friend: someone who is a good listener, empathetic, and respectful, as well as keeps their promises. The take-home message is be kind.

To list even more ways to be a true friend, please unscramble the words found at the bottom of the page, then insert them into the crossword puzzle. The answers are on page 145.

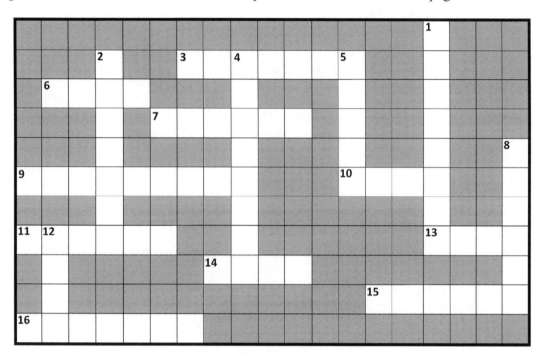

GOOD FRIENDS:

ACROSS

3. UPTROPS _____ each other's goals (to stand by someone)

6. Bring out the OGDO _____ in the other person (opposite to bad)

7. ISNETL _____ to one another (using ears in a conversation)

9. Be VABAILLEA _____ (to be present when needed)

10. Spend enough MIET _____ together (what a clock measures)

11. EPTCAC _____ one another (be okay with the goods and bads)

13. make it SEAF _____ to speak one's mind (when no harm comes to you)

14. Help LEAH _____ (improve health)

15. Have a positive RGRDEA _____ for each other (optimists believe in this)

16. PETCSER _____ each other's needs (to care and treat others right)

DOWN

1. Act with KIDNNSSE _____ (to treat someone with passion)

2. ORGFVIE _____ each others' mistakes (to not hold anything against)

4. Have PIENATEC _____ (ability to wait a long time)

5. RSUTT _____ each other (believe the other person's word)

8. We all need a DNREFI _____ (when you have a connection with somebody)

12. RECA _____ about each other's well-being (when it matters to you)

DAY 22. ASSERTIVE COMMUNICATION

PURPOSE OF THIS WORKSHEET:

- To hit you over the head with assertive communication skills.
- Okay, not hit over head. But we gotta share this stuff.

HOW DO YOU APPROACH OTHERS? Do you help people at all costs, or is this an eye-for-an-eye world, where you can't trust a single soul? Or do you do something different? Not sure? No problem, we're here to help. Introducing the "How do you talk when you talk?" Quiz.

1. Which of the following best matches your communication style?   A   B   C   D

   a. Other people's needs are more important than mine. In fact, I tend to put myself down to make others feel better.
   b. I believe everyone's needs are important, including mine.
   c. I'm competitive and get nasty when I need to. After all, if I don't take care of my needs, who will?
   d. I tried standing on my head once. That didn't work.

2. Which of the following best matches your body language?   A   B   C   D

   a. I tend to avoid eye contact and hunch over to make myself less intimidating to others.
   b. I tend to be confident but kind-looking. Or at least I try.
   c. I stare and intimidate people because that's the only way to get people to respect you.
   d. Like I said, headstand.

3. You have a disabled neighbor you help on the weekends. Lately he's expecting you to help every day, which you really can't do. You need time to yourself. What do think about the situation?   A   B   C   D

   a. He can't help himself, and if I were in his position, I'd be asking for help too. I'm being selfish if I don't agree to show up at least a few hours every day.
   b. He has needs, but I do too. I need time to relax after work. I say NO to "everyday" and ask him to look for additional people to help him. I'm available weekends.
   c. Just because he's disabled, it doesn't mean he has the right to demand all my time. What a twerp. I should call his case manager and let them know he's drinking.
   d. What does this have to do with a headstand?

4. Your ex-wife wants you to care for the kids this weekend. She has an important job interview. But you already have plans to watch the whole season of *Love in the City*. What do you do?   A   B   C   D

   a. I'm independently wealthy and feel guilty about it. Of course, I take the kids. I'll also pay for my ex-wife and her new husband to fly to the city where the interview is held.

   b. I love *Love in the City*, but my ex's interview is more important. I'll cancel my plans and watch the kids.

   c. I'm not helping that woman no matter what, not after what she did to me. I'll send her an intimidating email, with bad words and some threats. She needs to stay away.

   d. My ex-wife can't do a headstand, but her cartwheels are divine; I'd go ahead and watch the kids.

5. Your homeless son asks for money to buy a cell phone so potential employers can call him. Every time you've said no in the past, he gets angry. What do you think about the situation?   A   B   C   D

   a. He'll get angry regardless of what I do. But he needs a job to improve his life. So I'll buy him the cell phone.
   b. I'm not going to let him intimidate me into paying for his cell phone. I'll offer a ride to interviews, but that's all. It's not my fault he gets upset.
   c. If he thinks I'm getting him another cell phone – or anything – he's an idiot. He's not taking advantage of me. He's not worth the ground he walks on.
   d. Honestly, I'm sick of talking about headstands. And C was really nasty.

INTERPRETATION

To figure out your communication style, review your answers and determine which letter you circled the most: A, B, C, or D? Match your letter with the one below.

A. **The "You're okay, I'm not okay" Style.**

   WHAT→Also called Passive Communication, you tend to go along with the demands of others, even let them walk all over you, to avoid "rocking the boat." It's possible you worry people won't like you if you say what's on your mind.

   RECOMMENDATION→ Start by standing up for your needs, the more important ones. You'll discover the world doesn't end, and, in fact, people treat you better.

B. **The "You're okay, I'm okay" Style.**

   WHAT → This style is also called Assertive Communication. You have a firm but gentle way about you. You are respectful and empathetic and direct, use non-blaming words, and stand up for your needs as well as the needs of others.

   RECOMMENDATIONS → Keep doing what you're doing!

C. **The "You're not okay, I'm okay" Style**

   WHAT → (C) describes Aggressive Communication. Do you focus on your own needs so much that you sometimes hurt others? Do you use anger to get your way? Do you tend to blame others? If so, you're using aggression to get your needs met.

   RECOMMENDATIONS → Start out with treatment for anger management. Also, try to see things from other people's perspective.

D. **Fake news.** (D) is nothing but ridiculous, and we don't advise headstands or any acrobatic positions be used as a primary communication style. Please go back, take the quiz again, and choose different answers. Thanks.

I have superb communication skills, with expert body language and a voice that will make you swoon. I've got it all. I can turn a criminal into a saint, convince a dragon to act like a puppy, and bring all wars to an end. I can also stand on my head, but that's another story.

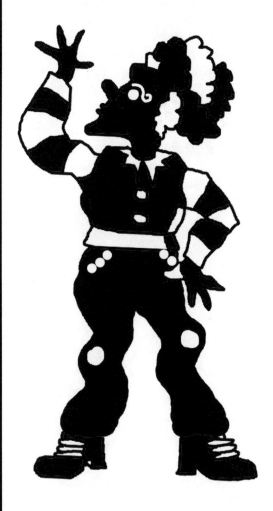

SOLVING CONFLICT ASSERTIVELY. **Here's the important stuff!**

1. **Listen and repeat.** First, pay attention to the other person's request. Next, repeat it back to them, making sure you understand. "I think you're saying…"
2. **State your request clearly.** Keep your head up and voice calm. "My request is…"
3. **Don't focus on always "winning."** Be willing to collaborate, if that's what's necessary. Consider different options. "I can do ___ if you do ___…"

For each of the scenarios below, write an assertive reaction using all 3 steps.

For example, imagine your roommate keeps eating your cookies without buying more.

Assertive reaction: "I think you're saying it's hard to avoid the cookies when they're in plain sight?" "I can hide them if you want, so you won't be tempted, or you give me 3 dollars/week for a cookie fund."

SCENARIOS

Someone is stealing your backyard tomatoes, and you've caught them on video. It's a neighborhood teenager whose parents don't give him enough food. What do you do?

You came home with a new motorcycle today, and your wife is upset that you didn't buy her one too. But you don't have money to buy another. How do you respond? She's typically easy-going, so don't worry yourself sick over this one.

Your neighbor has taken up drums, which he insists on playing at 2 in the morning. You have a job and need to sleep at night. What do you do?

Your answer

Your answer

Your answer

EXTRA CREDIT: ADVANCED
ASSERTIVENESS SKILLS

The coolest, smartist, and most effective form of communication is the assertive style, so it's worthwhile spending more time here. Here are some pointers.

POINTERS

Try to improve the situation, not make it worse. Don't insult, threaten, or use aggression. It might intimidate people and help you get your way, but it creates disrespect and resentment.

Use "I" instead of "YOU" statements. Instead of saying, "You really piss me off when you say things like that" (i.e. everything is your fault!), say "I get angry when I hear people say things like that" (this removes blame).

Know when to say YES, NO, or something different. To make sure, weigh your needs against the other person's needs: Who has more to lose?

If the other person has more to lose → Grant their request
If both needs are equally important → Compromise
If you have more to lose than the other person → Insist

REFLECTION

Think of a situation in your life where there's some disagreement. You want one thing, and the other person wants something else. In the space below, describe an assertive way to approach the problem.

DAY 23. GOOD VS BAD RELATIONSHIPS

PURPOSE OF THIS WORKSHEET:

- Identify unhealthy relationships
- Learn strategies to deal with them

IMAGINE

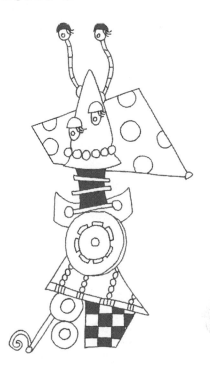

Imagine you're an alien. You're a rare creature from the planet Gaborb, so rare that you're the only member of your species that's ever existed. You've been on your own for as long as you can remember.

Then suddenly you discover humans, and humans are weird: they like each other's company. "Fabobbles," you think and devote 35,000 years to human observation.

1. What's strange about an alien who's lived in isolation all his life? Choose more than one.

    a. If he doesn't have a mother, where did he come from?
    b. How does this species reproduce? Is he really male?
    c. How could the alien develop language if no one ever taught him?
    d. What does this have to do with toxic relationships?
    e. An alien… really?

All of the above are valid questions. We ask you to suspend disbelief and imagine you're an alien watching humans interact. Thanks. Move onto #2.

2. In the beginning, Earth makes no sense to you. Humans interact senselessly, without any clear reason. What are you really seeing? Choose one.

    a. All love and sweetness.
    b. All violence and war.
    c. Objective, nonjudgmental interactions.
    d. Boy, all sorts of stuff. Billions of unique relationships.

3. You've been studying humans for 3 minutes and now recognize the difference between good and bad relationships. Which of the following are **healthy** interactions? Choose more than one.

    a. A woman complains that it's a friend's fault she's unhappy.
    b. A man makes his friend feel better about himself.
    c. A woman convinces her friend that he's flawed and crazy.
    d. A woman makes sure she listens to her friend. Conversation should go both ways.

4. Which of the following are **harmful** interactions? Choose more than one.

    a.   A mother refuses to help her father get his driver's license back after he loses it from dangerous driving.

    b.   A man's older brother won't let him work or have contact with others, including their parents and other siblings.

    c.   A daughter threatens to kill herself if her parents won't do what she wants.

    d.   A boss tells his employees that they should work carefully.

So what's the difference between good and bad relationships? Here are two dancing couples to help clarify the issue. Read through the tips, then go to #5 below.

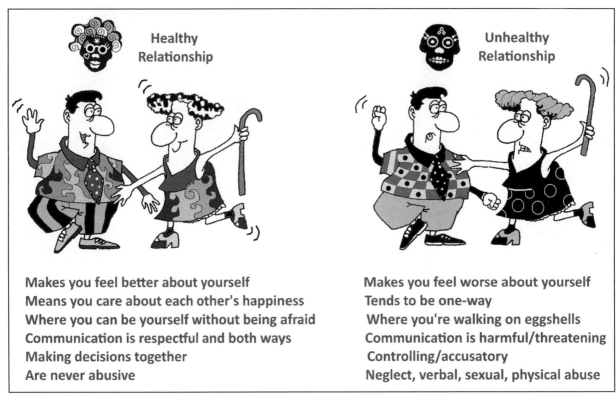

Healthy Relationship	Unhealthy Relationship
Makes you feel better about yourself	Makes you feel worse about yourself
Means you care about each other's happiness	Tends to be one-way
Where you can be yourself without being afraid	Where you're walking on eggshells
Communication is respectful and both ways	Communication is harmful/threatening
Making decisions together	Controlling/accusatory
Are never abusive	Neglect, verbal, sexual, physical abuse

Healthy relationships promote the well-being
of both parties. Toxic relationships hurt.

5. Back to being an alien. You have a human-looking outfit and decide to go down to Earth to make some friends. Three minutes later, you've made 100 friends. Unfortunately, you have 8 unhealthy relationships. These friends are demeaning, threatening, controlling, or accusatory, or all of the above. What's a good way to deal with an unhealthy connection?

    a.   Spend time with the other person out of pity

    b.   Try to convince them to be nice, even though it never works

    c.   Give into their demands to avoid rocking the boat

    d.   Talk to a friend to get advice

    e.   Spread false rumors about them to get revenge.

ANSWERS

1. All answers are appropriate.
2. (D) is correct. Humans are neither all good or all violent, and they're definitely not always objective. There are many factors that go into a relationship, and chances are each connection is unique.
3. (B) and (D) are right. The other two are characteristics of toxic relationships.
4. (B) and (C) are examples of unhealthy interactions. Keeping a driver's license away from a dangerous driver (A) is appropriate, as is (D) a boss instructing staff to be careful in their work.
5. The right answer is (D). The other options don't improve the situation.

YOUR RELATIONSHIPS

If you can describe your relationship as disrespectful, demeaning, disruptive, exhausting, unsafe, or abusive, it's probably toxic. The nastiness can go one or both ways.

Healthy relationships promote mutual well-being, like what you have with your best friend. "In-between" is a connection that needs a bit of work, like an uncle who lectures you all the time.

In the space below, decide whether the relationships in your life are healthy, toxic, or something in between. Remember, no relationship is perfect.

Healthy Relationship	In Between	Toxic Relationship
Promotes well-being	Good and bad	Destructive and exhausting
Examples: Someone who's always there for you, a friend who supports you through tough situations.	Examples: Boss who's too strict, aunt who keeps giving you money, father who doesn't understand addiction	Examples: Using friend, abusive partner, colleague who blames you for everything, explosive mother

3. DEALING WITH TOXIC RELATIONSHIPS

Read through the following, then answer the Reflection question at the bottom.

HOW DO YOU DEAL WITH THE UNHEALTHY PEOPLE IN YOUR LIFE?

We recommend talking to someone you trust and leaving the relationship when it's safe to do so. Here are more suggestions.

- **Believe in yourself.** Nobody deserves to be treated badly.

- **If there's abuse, call the National Domestic Violence Hotline at 800 799 7233.** Alternatively, call the police.

- **Communicate assertively.** Be respectful, but take care of your needs. See Day 22 for more information.

- **Survival skills.** Toxic relationships are exhausting. Make sure to learn strategies to help you heal. Examples include positive self-talk, meditation for anxiety, and keeping a Gratitude List.

- **Set healthy limits.** Make conscious decisions to protect yourself and improve the situation. See below.

LIMIT SETTING

LIMITS ARE BOUNDARIES CREATED TO PROTECT YOU AND IMPROVE THE SITUATION. IT ISN'T PUNISHMENT.

EXAMPLES OF SETTING LIMITS

→ Cut off all contact if needed
→ If you can't avoid them, limit time spent together
→ Decide to not meet alone
→ Not tolerating abuse: hang up the phone, walk away, call the police, etc.
→ As long as it's safe, say NO when you need to.

REFLECTION

Choose a problem relationship in your life and, using this worksheet as a guide, come up with healthy ways to deal with the situation.

TAKE A BREAK RECOVERY ART

WHAT RECOVERY MEANS TO YOU

**YOU'RE GOING TO CAPTURE SOBRIETY ON PAPER. RATHER THAN WORDS,
DRAW 12 PICTURES SYMBOLIZING RECOVERY IN EACH OF THE 12 SPACES BELOW.**

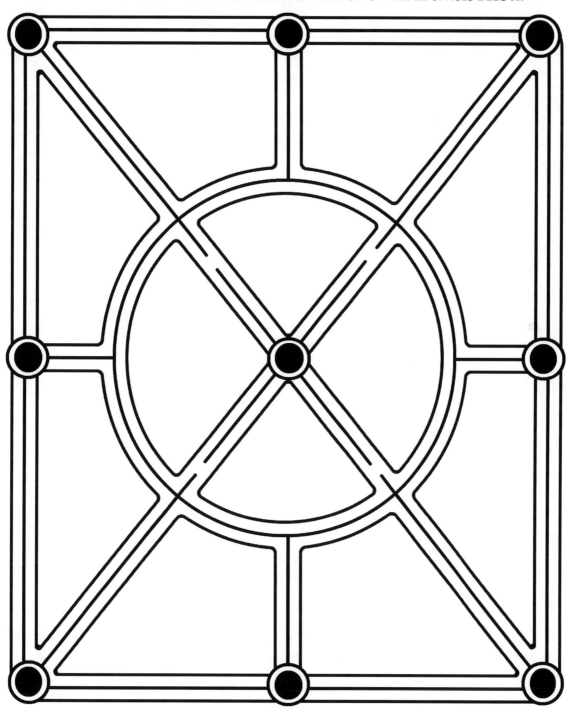

DAY 24. ASTOUNDING WORLD

PURPOSE OF THIS WORKSHEET:

- To focus on the astounding things you've experienced
- To explore identity and experience

"I'VE SEEN GREAT THINGS YOU WOULDN'T BELIEVE."

PART ONE: The above is a butchered quotation from the movie Blade Runner. The character is dying, and in his last moments he shares his greatest experiences, things that for him made life worthwhile.

We've all had stunning moments. Sometimes you have to think hard to find them, but they're there. What greatness have you seen? What memories, sights, people, and truths have you known that made life worthwhile? Using sentences like "I've seen…" and "I've known," fill the space below with what inspires you.

PART TWO: Once you've finished PART ONE, use your answers to fill in the next page. Stick with your best handwriting, and consider coloring the design. When finished, keep the handout in a place you see often. Read every day.

I'VE SEEN GREAT THINGS YOU WOULDN'T BELIEVE

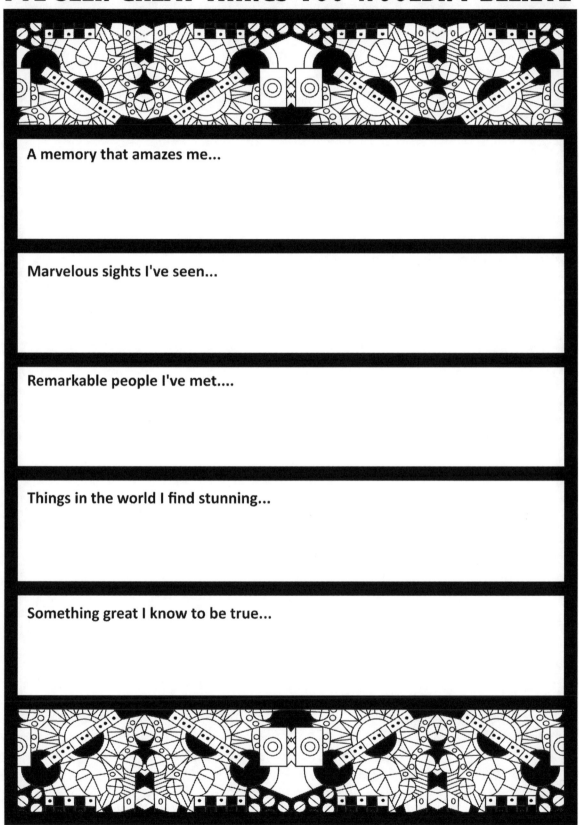

A memory that amazes me...

Marvelous sights I've seen...

Remarkable people I've met....

Things in the world I find stunning...

Something great I know to be true...

REFLECTION

How did this exercise make you feel?

Out of all the things you wrote about, what stuck out the most? Why?

How can you better pay attention to the beauty around you?

Why remember the things that make life worth living? In truth, it's an odd question, but sometimes we forget -- especially during rough moments, when all the feel-good stuff goes down the drain. Remember, when overrun with pain and negativity, look to the parts of your life that make you go "WOW." Or just reread this worksheet.

On Day 25, we explore the good stuff again, but in a different way. Stay tuned.

DAY 25. A WELL-LIVED LIFE

PURPOSE OF THIS WORKSHEET:

- To introduce the future as an exciting place
- To make room for goals and dreams

A WELL-LIVED LIFE

Imagine you're 100 years old and looking back on a life well-lived. You've overcome all obstacles. You've achieved everything you hoped to achieve. You feel completely fulfilled and joyful to have experienced everything you did. What would that life look like? What problems did you solve? What dreams and goals did you fulfill? Write about your 100-year-old life here, making sure *it's incompatible with drugs and alcohol.* Make it awesome too.

You've written about the life you want, and that's a big deal. Now we need specifics. Keep writing, using the following questions as prompts.

Who did you love?	Where did you travel?
Where did you go?	What did you learn?
Did you have grandkids?	How did you find meaning?

REFLECTION

It's important to imagine and record the type of life you want. It gives your brain a template for action, a direction to move. Apart from staying clean and sober, how can you start making this future happen *today*? Here are some ideas.

Complete this worksheet	Make a list of dreams	Google "plan my future"
Spend time with people I love	Think about one goal	Complete one small chore
Do something I love	Work on one problem	Go to a 12-Step meeting

What are **your** ideas? Pile on a few here!

FINALE, WHEN YOU FINISH THIS BOOK

PURPOSE OF THIS WORKSHEET:

- To review everything
- To remember growth

TASK ONE

You've had quite a journey! But how much do you remember? Review the list below and cross out the options that are **not** covered in this book.

a. How to make a schedule	b. A theater production saying NO
c. A list of interesting phone apps	d. The beauty of being you
e. Recognizing and rewriting problem thoughts	f. A bunch of ways to deal with cravings and triggers
g. A song by the Rolling Stones	h. A listening exercise
i. A story about a talking box	j. Instructions to build a log home
k. A chance to map your life on paper	l. A story about a lonely alien
m. You get kidnapped and wake up in a jungle with a moody friend	n. You learn to say the word "detox" in Spanish: "Desintoxicacion"
o. A chance to meet an emotion	p. You explore your past and future

What do you think? Topics not covered include (G, J, and N). All others, including phone apps, talking boxes, jungles, and theater productions were part of this book.

TASK TWO

Things were different a month ago.

You've changed. You've learned from the past. You've faced the NOW, practicing ways to calm cravings and get past painful emotion. You've explored thought and behaviors. You've also replaced addiction with something worthwhile, worked on your new identity, and stopped to remember your own goodness.

Got all that? On the next page, write a speech introducing the new sober YOU to the world. Write your name on the provided line, then fill the page with words of achievement, growth, and potential. When finished, share it with someone – or set it in front of the bathroom mirror and read it out loud at random moments. Remember who you really are.

(Coloring is optional.)

HI. MY NAME IS _____, AND THIS IS THE
SOBER NEW ME. I AM...

REFLECTION

Part of creating a sober new identity is filling the void in your life. What's replaced addiction? Make sure this "what" is something you love, something healthy and fun and worthwhile.

So, for you, what's replaced addiction? It might be going through old photographs or cuddling with your puppy. Or it can be something larger, like studying to become a photographer or training your puppy to mind read.* Whatever it is, write it out in big bubble letters below, then decorate the letters with doodles, giving them life. Go for it.

(Not sure what this is about? See Days 18 and 19 for more information.)

WRAP UP

This book is finished, but you aren't! Your journey goes on. You'll climb the heights of great mountains, dip to the deepest sea, and it'll be hard and tiring. But you'll also find joy in who you are, what you surround yourself with, and in a future filled with great potential – if only you reach for it. Go forth and live!

Oh, miss us already? No worries, there are more pictures to draw, stories to write, puzzles to solve, strange scenarios to decipher, and questions to answer! Check out the original *Outside-the-Box Recovery Workbook*, available on Amazon books. There's more information on page 164. Thanks, and see you soon!

---

*Dogs are not able to read minds. Anyone who tells you differently is probably wrong (woof).

ONE MORE BREAK, GO FOR IT!

What happens next is up to you. Make it a good one! In the meantime, can you determine which cartoon comes next? The answer is found on page 146.

BONUS WORKSHEETS

COPING SKILLS: THE "DID IT WORK?" CARD

PURPOSE OF THIS WORKSHEET:

- To practice skills
- To figure out which skills are the most helpful

THE "DID IT WORK?" CARD

On the next page, you'll find a coping skill assessment form. It's a great way to establish that clients are practicing coping mechanisms: whether in class or as homework, request a completed form after the skill or exercise is performed. As a motivating force, randomly hand out chocolates or gum or stickers or thumb wars (yes!) to those who actually do them.

This worksheet can be an "on-the-spot" exercise or used to monitor the effect of a specific coping skill over time.

Instructions are easy enough. Clients should fill in the blanks. For example, if the skill is gratitude, have clients complete Day 14 (The Gratitude List). When finished, ask them to complete the "DID IT WORK?" card. They should record how they felt before and after the task, as well as add personal comments and rate the activity.

DISCUSSION

The final box is a place to mingle. Here's where conversation takes place. When do you need coping skills? How can you work more of them into your life? When, how, and how often? When do you start?

Questions can be more challenging. If there's a lot of resistance to completing this form, that's a perfect place to start. There are more questions: Skills usually get better with practice, but not always; how many times must you practice a skill before ditching it? (Answers will differ.) What kinds of situations require coping strategies? Is it possible to use one skill for everything?

THE "DID IT WORK?" CARD

We recommend you use this card every time you practice a coping skill in this book. Fill out each box, including date, activity, and how you felt before and after the experience.

Date:
Activity:
Time spent:

How did you feel before the activity? Describe and rate the emotion.

I felt: _____

Argh, life is awful.   Yay, life is awesome!

1   2   3   4   5   6   7   8   9   10

How did you feel after the activity? Describe and rate the emotion.

I felt: _____

Argh, life is awful.   Yay, life is awesome!

1   2   3   4   5   6   7   8   9   10

How did this activity go for you? What worked, what didn't? Why?

What's your overall rating for this skill?

Argh, it made things worse!   Yay, it was fabulous!

1   2   3   4   5   6   7   8   9   10

Skills usually get more effective with practice. If you want, how can you work this type of activity into your life? When, how, and how often? When do you start?

MOTIVATION: DO YOU WANT TO QUIT?

PURPOSE OF THIS WORKSHEET:

- Help contemplative clients explore the idea of quitting drugs

MOTIVATIONAL INTERVIEWING

This 3-page form uses motivational interviewing to engage clients in an important discussion: Whether quitting drugs is right for them. It's illustrated, informal, nonjudgmental, and humored.

INSTRUCTIONS

This worksheet is generally self-explanatory. Go to "START HERE" and follow the arrows. As the arrows move from box to box, encourage clients to answer all questions in writing.

Pages 130-131 give clients the option to leave or stay and finish the worksheet. Pre-contemplative and contemplative people (and anyone who opts to leave) are invited to page through the book, finish puzzles, read anything that seems interesting, and come back later when they're ready. There's no pressure. "We'll keep the lights on for you." Those ready to embrace recovery continue onto page 132, which touches on motivation and change.

Anecdotally, this is a good initial tool to use with new clients.

MOTIVATION: DO YOU WANT TO QUIT?

This form uses motivational interviewing to help explore the concept of quitting drugs.

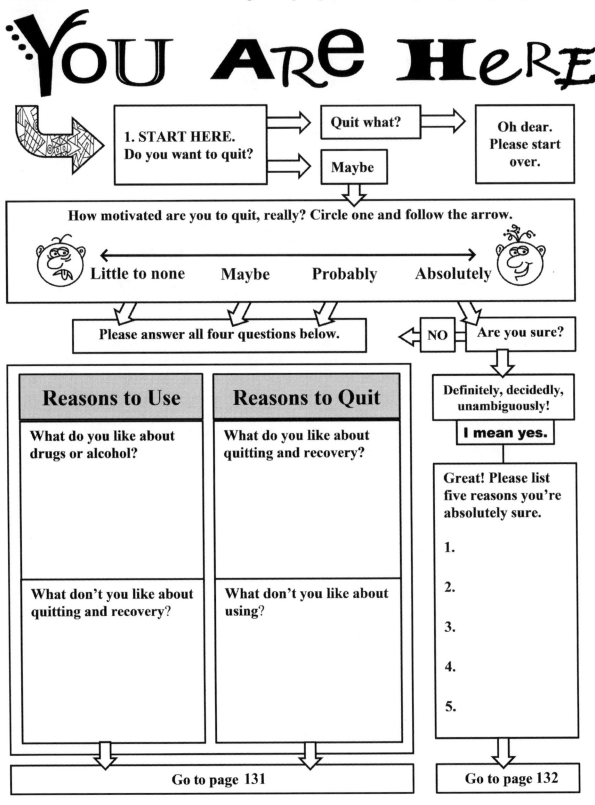

You Are still Here

(Continued.) On p130, you wrote two lists. Is there anything to add? Go back and review each list, adding any ideas that come to mind. Consider family, friends, love, school, health, and mental well-being. Use additional paper if needed.

Ooooooh, Too much thinking

Next, compare your lists by answering the four questions below.

Of the two, which list is longer? (Circle one of the lists on the right.)	REASON TO USE	REASON TO QUIT
Which list seems more convincing?	REASON TO USE	REASON TO QUIT
Which list would someone who cares about you recommend?	REASON TO USE	REASON TO QUIT
Which list would most likely help you pursue your dreams?	REASON TO USE	REASON TO QUIT

So, what's the verdict? Which list carries the most "oomph?" Choose from the options below.

Option 1: Keep using

Not ready to quit? Fair enough. We respect that. You're in the driver's seat, so it's your decision. For now, consider paging through this book and laughing at the corny jokes before you go. Come back when you're ready. We'll leave the light on for you.

Option 2: Quit using

Congrats, you've quit -- or you're thinking about it! We're excited you're here!! Please take off your jacket and hang out a while. Rest a bit before going onto the next page...

YOU ARE FINISHED

REFLECTION

You made it, and in good time! This worksheet was about motivation. Motivation means deciding to (maybe) quit using and drinking -- and accepting help to do so! You've made a huge step in that direction. Motivation is also about an openness to change, but that's mostly for a different day. For now, please answer the following questions as best you can.

1. How motivated are you to quit/stay quit, now that you've finished this worksheet? If you don't choose "absolutely," that's okay. What will it take for you to move in that direction?

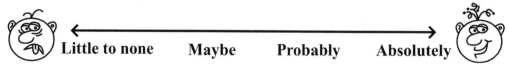

Little to none   **Maybe**   **Probably**   **Absolutely**

2. How ready are you to live a sober and clean life? If you don't choose absolutely, that's okay. Just keep an open mind.

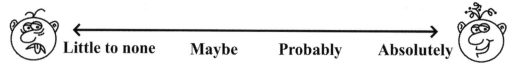

Little to none   **Maybe**   **Probably**   **Absolutely**

3. Can a person recover from drugs and alcohol without doing things differently? (Please outline the "NO" below, doodle in some design, then provide one reason change might be necessary.)

That's it for now. If you haven't yet, make sure to discuss your answers with your counselor. Thanks!

APPENDICES

APPENDIX A. ANSWERS

TAKE A BREAK. THE "NO" SIGN, PAGE 21

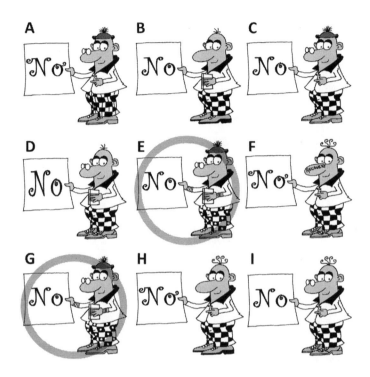

DAY 4. HAVE HOPE, PAGE 29

You are capable of great things.

TAKE A BREAK. BRAIN STUFF, PAGE 32

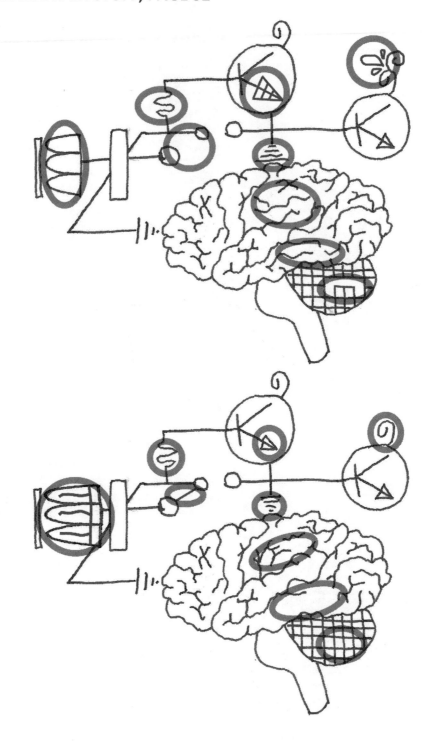

TAKE A BREAK. PUZZLES THAT SAY NO, PAGE 44

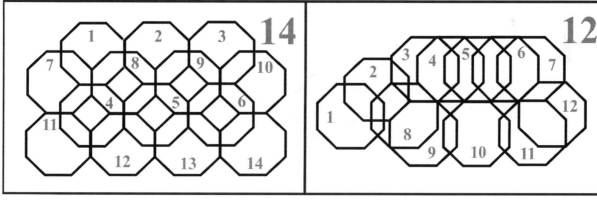

DAY 8. DEALING WITH TRIGGERS 1, TRIGGER MAZE, PAGE 48

WHICH START
FINISHES THE
MAZE?

START #1

START #2

START #3

START #4

START #5

START #6

END

DAY 9. TRIGGERS TO AVOID WORD SEARCH, PAGE 52

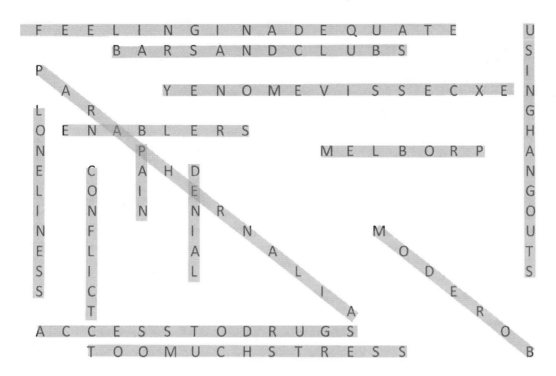

DAY 10. WORDS IN "AVOID TRIGGER," PAGE 54

There are 100's of words. Here are some we found.

Age	Dare	E-gad	Gore	Ova	Rid	Tear	Trod
Aged	Dig	Ego	Great	Overt	Ride	Tide	Varied
Aid	Dire	Ear	Grid	Radio	Rig	Tire	Vat
Are	Dried	Goat	Grit	Rag	Rod	Tired	Void
Ave	Drier	Get	Ire	Rage	Rot	Tore	Vote
Avert	Eat	God	Ired	Rat	Rote	Tried	

Words at the bottom:

Great	Got	Driver	Air	Raider	Red	Dog/god

TAKE A BREAK: DIFFERENT ROADS TO RECOVERY, PAGE 58

There are 15 differences.

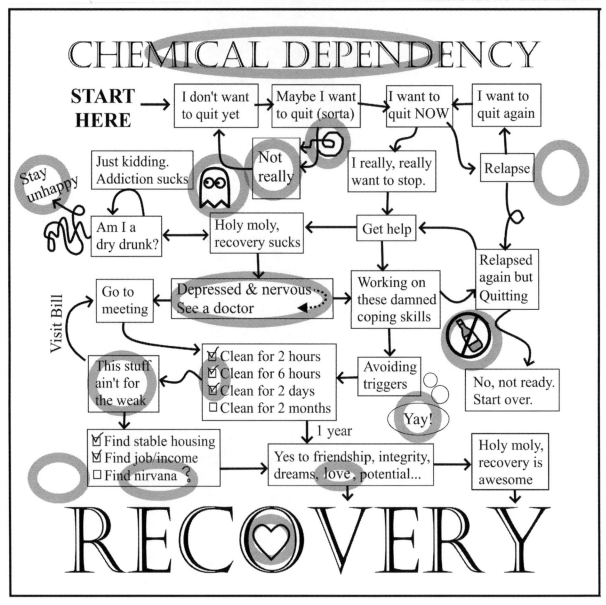

DAY 10. WORDS IN "GRATITUDE LIST," PAGE 72

There are 100's of words. Here are some we found.

Ads	Dire	Great	Rage/rages	Silt	Suite	Trade/trades
Age/ages	Due/dues	Guide/guides	Rat/rats	Sir	Sud	Trait/traits
Aid/aids	Duet/duets	Gut/guts	Rate/rates	Sit	Taste/tastes	
Are	Duties	Lad/lads	Rude	Stat	Tier/tiers	
Ate	Gist	Lie/lies/lied	Sat	Stir	Tile/tiles	
Date/dates	Grate/grates	Lute/lutes	Sad	Suit	Tire/tires	

DAY 11. SURVIVAL STRATEGIES WORD SEARCH, PAGE 62

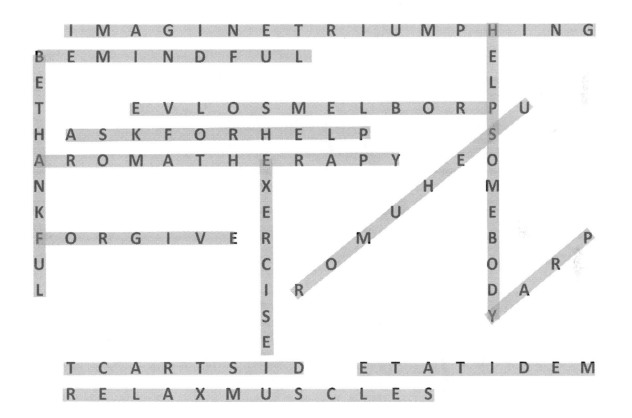

TAKE A BREAK. THE MAZE OF HOPE, PAGE 78

TAKE A BREAK. SHE SAID NO, PAGE 86

DAY 18. REPLACING DRUGS WITH THE GOOD STUFF CODE, PAGE 89

DAY 20. TRUST WORD SEARCH, PAGE 100

DAY 21. GOOD FRIEND CROSSWORD PUZZLE, PAGE 105

```
                                              ¹K
        ²F        ³S  U  ⁴P  P  O  R  ⁵T       I
    ⁶G  O  O  D           A           R        N
        R     ⁷L  I  S  T  E  N       U        D
        G              I           S        N        ⁷F
⁹A  V  A  I  L  A  B  L  E        ¹⁰T  I  M  E        R
        V              N                    S        I
¹¹A ¹²C  C  E  P  T        C              ¹²S  A  F  E
    A           ¹⁴H  E  A  L                        N
    R                          ¹⁵R  E  G  A  R  D
¹⁶R  E  S  P  E  C  T
```

ACROSS

3. Support
6. Good
7. Listen
9. Available
10. Time
11. Accept
12. Safe
14. Heal
15. Regard
16. Respect

DOWN

1. Kindness
2. Forgive
4. Patience
5. Trust
7. Friend
12. Care

ONE MORE BREAK: GO FOR IT, PAGE 124

APPENDIX B: INFO FOR PROFESSIONALS

BACKGROUND

My name is Kim Rosenthal, MD. I'm a psychiatrist with over 2 decades of experience working in the mental health field. Professionally, I've worked in a variety of settings, including alcohol and substance abuse treatment centers (ADATC's), detox units, rehabs, day hospitals, clinics, inpatient hospitalization, forensic hospitals, and veteran healthcare.

As a physician. I practice evidence-based medicine and conform to standard of care. As a multi-modal professional, I believe in the power of therapeutic interaction and the many disciplines needed to help people with addiction. Relapse prevention is important. 12-step programming, cognitive behavioral therapy, motivational interviewing, Matrix Model, psychoeducation, and coping skill training are all important. These are just some of the modalities we use to take on substance use disorders, and studies show they make a difference.

But we need more than mainstream modalities. In the age of COVID, where isolation and addiction are more rampant than ever, we desperately need evidence-based treatment options that are... outside-the-box. That means narrative therapy. It also means creative writing, art therapy, coloring mindfulness, and positive psychology. Why outside-the-box? Because it works! Research shows that combining mainstream treatment with these extra approaches + fun increase retention and lower relapse rate (Beaufort 2017; Eschleman et al 2014; McKay 2016). That means we can improve patient outcomes by supplementing mainstream care with optimism, creativity, art, and the occasional joke. These modalities don't replace traditional treatment. They augment them. To find out more about *Outside-the-Box Recovery*, visit kimrosenthalmd.com.

COMBINING TRADITIONAL AND EVIDENCE-BASED NON-TRADITIONAL TREATMENT IMPROVES RETENTION AND LOWERS RELAPSE RATE.	
Examples of Traditional Treatment	*Examples of Nontraditional Treatment*
Motivational interviewing	Art therapy
Relapse prevention	Narrative therapy
Cognitive behavioral therapy	Expressive therapy
Matrix model	Creative writing
Mindfulness	Poetry therapy
Psychoeducation	Positive psychology
Coping and life skills training	Cognitive remediation
Medication management	Coloring mindfulness
Strength-based treatment	Journaling
Contingency management	Humor

Combining different treatment modalities improves patient outcomes.

ABOUT THIS BOOK

The SECOND *Outside-the-Box Recovery Workbook* combines both traditional and non-traditional modalities to help people survive drugs and alcohol use disorders. It's written for addiction counselors and their clients, as well as anyone in early recovery.

Worksheets take on recognizable themes:

- Grieving addiction's role in one's life
- Dealing with cravings and triggers
- Soothing tough emotions: Mindfulness, gratitude, and journaling
- Rewriting problem thoughts and behaviors
- Keeping a schedule
- Enhancing interpersonal skills and communicating assertively
- Recognizing self-worth

The book includes 25 handouts, each 2-5 pages in length. That translates into five weeks of group or individual work. At the beginning, you'll find a Recovery Plan. The end includes two bonus worksheets (coping skill efficacy and motivational interviewing), answers to all puzzles, as well as this Professional Section and the Bibliography.

Here are some general recommendations when using the book.

- For drug & alcohol counselors, the workbook may be used as primary therapist-driven treatment or to augment other approaches. In general, handouts can be presented in any order. Most can be done in one session.
- Clients should do **all** exercises in writing. This shows they're doing the work, plus there's something powerful and solid about writing things down. If they won't document their thoughts, the resistance is grist for the mill. Look for the source and help get them past it. You can also use simple incentives to reward those who do the work, like a cookie, cup of coffee, permission to chew gum in group, or a chance to share a favorite (healthy-version) song. Alternatively, for anyone who misbehaves, just temporarily keep their shoes! This works well with younger groups, anyway.
- These worksheets tend to be longer than those in the first book. This gives clinicians a chance to pick and choose which parts to use, i.e. those which are more relevant, as well as optionally divide exercises into two days. That said, each exercise is written for a 45-60 minute session.
- All worksheets end with a Reflection Section. It brings the topic home, anchors important points, and can be a great platform for conversation.
- Occasionally, quizzes and other questions are answered on the same page; if this is the case, consider asking clients to fold the answers back until ready to review.
- There are nine "Take-a-Break" worksheets in the book, primarily puzzles. These can be used at the beginning or end of a session to "get people going" or as optional homework.
- If you wish to use both the first and second OTB Recovery Workbooks in your practice, you can mix them up or use them consecutively. Each book is different.

SPECIFIC HANDOUTS

RECOVERY PLAN 101, PAGE 5. *Relapse prevention* (Hendershot et al, 2011; Rawson et al, 2005; Witkiewitz et al, 2007), *making recovery more attractive* (McKay 2016). This recovery plan does two things. First, it focuses on the actual task of quitting drugs and alcohol. Second, the plan carries readers through a sequence of questions that points to different parts of the workbook. Jumping ahead is entirely optional, but if there are some questions that weigh more heavily than others, this is a great opportunity to focus on what matters first.

DAY 1. WHY RECOVERY? PAGE 13. *Relapse prevention, art therapy* (Aletraris et al, 2014; Matto 2002; Matto et al, 2013; Sharp, 2018; Wilson, 2012). This worksheet explores reasons to quit and choose recovery. For the first exercise, clients should review the table and check the reasons that apply to them – and cross out all bad reasons. Both good and bad reasons make room for discussion – Is other people telling you to quit enough? Do you have to hit bottom before choosing recovery? If you're taking prescribed Methadone, are you still using drugs? The next activity involves two open windows. The top window looks into life while the client was using. The second is a reflection of recovery, or if they haven't quit, the idea of recovery. Bypass words and aim for the nonverbal: Ask clients to draw what they imagine. Provide colors and music if you want! Once pics are complete, use the reflection questions to pull things together. Note that people can balk at drawing exercises, but once they submerge themselves in the task, they're often surprised with what they find.

DAY 2. MEMORIES OF ADDICTION, PAGE 17. *Poetry therapy* (Kreuter, 2020; Springer, 2006; Williamson et al, 2018). Writing is a potent way to explore the pain of addiction – but not an easy task. Not everyone will ascribe to poetry, so broaden your scope by embracing song lyrics, rap, essays, nonfiction, cartoons, and even fiction. You can even have clients cut pictures out of old magazines and stick them together in a meaningful way. Make sure patients avoid words that put drugs/alcohol in a positive light. Examples include describing drug paraphernalia or the joy of injecting. *More importantly, encourage clients to avoid writing about anything they wish to avoid, like traumatic experiences.* Be available to anyone who needs to talk. Once finished, have clients add a positive ending… this is crucial!

DAY 3. YOUR LIFE SO FAR, PAGE 22. *Self-narration* (Kougiali et al, 2017; McConnell et al, 2018). Like Day 2, this handout helps clients revisit their past and put bad experiences into context, but this time the focus broadens to include good experiences and what they did right. It's a factual rendering of their story. Encourage them to answer all questions then use the answers to record their life as if it were a road on a map. There's an optional legend of symbols to represent different types of experiences, like mountains for obstacles, suns for happy moments, etc. Make sure clients don't get stuck on past trauma. If this is a potential concern, add some positive milestones, like when they adopted their first pet, earned their first paycheck, or received their first kiss. Use the reflection questions to create discussion. Explore the importance of knowing one's own story, especially the good stuff. Sharing is optional.

DAY 4. SATISFIED WITH LIFE? PAGE 26. *Life satisfaction* (Swain et al, 2012; Zullig et al, 2001). Day 4 takes on life satisfaction. Often people in early recovery aren't happy. They've struggled hard to quit, and they're finally here, but the world doesn't greet them with open arms. Now they have to deal with the aftermath of addiction. Now comes all the hard work. Before distributing the worksheet, ask clients their happiness score, between 1 "least happy" and 10 "most happy." Explore the reasons behind this number. What's going right? What needs to change? When ready, everyone should fill out the survey questions then stop to check their pulses. All alive? Ask them again: What's going right? What needs to change? The take-home point is simple. The trick to growth is to stop holding onto the bad stuff. Rather, make room for the good stuff. This leads to HOPE. Go through each question, then use the hope puzzle to close. We recommend avoiding a directed conversation about the laundry list of changes recovery entails. Emphasize staying clean, reaching out for help, and having hope. That's enough for now.

DAY 5. THE BEAUTY OF BEING YOU, PAGE 30. *Self-esteem* (Richter et al, 1991; Robins et al, 2012). Recovery is about hard work, yes, but it's also about self-compassion. Ask the group, "How do you talk to yourself during the darkest moments?" Answers will vary, but if honesty rules the day, many will admit self-compassion isn't always on the table. Strange, because that's when it's most needed. Ask clients to complete all eight statements. They shouldn't gloss over the details; challenge them to dig deep and push their responses as far as they'll go. This is about their greatness, and they need to *feel* it. Occasionally you'll meet individuals who are really struggling. To pre-emptively help anyone who needs it, emphasize that jotting down who they'd *like* to be is perfectly acceptable. Sharing their answers is optional. If you have extra time, consider brainstorming ways a person can improve self-compassion; if the group are at a loss, just have them search "how to improve self-compassion" on their phones. Give them examples of individuals who've overcome daunting obstacles, like Jessie Thistle and Gregory Smith (both went from homelessness to college professor) or Khalil Rhafati (homeless to million-dollar businessman).

DAY 6. DEALING WITH CRAVINGS 1, PAGE 33. *Relapse prevention, Matrix Model* (Rawson et al, 2005), *craving management* (Courbasson et al, 2002; Hendershot et al, 2011; Kavanagh et al, 2004). Day 6 introduces various urge-management techniques. The worksheet involves 4 exercises. (1) Answer the true/false questions about cravings, (2) decipher a list of statements about managing cravings, (3) match each urge-management technique to one of the examples provided, and (4) complete the Reflection Section. In the latter, clients should read the imaginary craving scenario and describe which technique(s) one might use to get past the urge.

DAY 7. DEALING WITH CRAVINGS 2, PAGE 39. *Relapse prevention, Matrix Model, craving management, writing therapy* (Bolton et al, 2004; Dingle et al, 2017; Kreuter, 2020; Pinhasi-Vittorio, 2018; Snead et al, 2015), *narrative therapy* (Diamond, 2002; Gardner et al, 2009; Garte-Wolf, 2011). This worksheet starts with the scenario questions on the first page. Clients will notice the repeated NO's, which introduces the purpose of Day 7: Just say NO! Page 2 focuses on nay-saying, and that brings us to the day's big task: *Writing a dialogue or play!* Patients should identify a personal high-risk situation where saying NO is absolutely necessary. When ready, hand out pages 3-5. The pages might look overwhelming, but at second glance the assignment is a no-brainer. The point is to write a dialogue saying NO as many times as they can. Patients should choose their preferred actor and setting, then push their way through Steps 3-5. Let them have fun! Life in practice! Review the reflection questions, then encourage them to share their work.

DAY 8. DEALING WITH CRAVINGS 3, PAGE 46. *Relapse prevention, Matrix Model, craving-management, SMART Recovery* (Alcohol & Drug Self-Help Network, 2013). Day 8 introduces the D.A.N.G. Urge-Management Technique. We recommend sharing the entire worksheet from the start. There are four components, and clients can use one at a time or all of them in one fowl swoop: (1) assign the craving a silly name, so as to separate it from self and diminish its power, (2) address the craving earlier than later, (3) say NO a bunch of times, and (4) distract for 30 minutes. Finally, have the group identify how they'd use D.A.N.G. to deal with the (triggering) scenario described under the Reflection.

DAY 9. RECOGNIZING TRIGGERS, PAGE 50. *Relapse prevention, Matrix Model, craving-management.* Clients in early recovery are especially sensitive to triggers. At this point in the game, let them know it's best to avoid triggers consciously, blatantly, and whole-heartedly (or deal with them if they can't be avoided). Page 1 presents several bizarre situations to bring the central idea home. The challenge is that you must identify triggers to be able to avoid them. The worksheet shifts into recognizing internal and external triggers, which are followed by a "List of Triggers" word search. To sum it all up, help clients identify their own triggers. Day 10 takes on the next step, managing triggers.

DAY 10. GETTING PAST TRIGGERS, PAGE 54. *Relapse prevention, Matrix Model, urge-management.* Day 10 is packed with information. If needed, divide it into two days. The worksheet is about handling unavoidable triggers, keeping in mind that the best strategy is to avoid triggers altogether. That said, hit clients over the head with the latter just a bit more: Have them create new words out of the phrase "AVOID TRIGGERS." Words at the bottom of page 1 include GREAT, GOT, DRIVER, AIR, DEAR/READ, and DOG/GOD. Determine who found the most words and reward them with a silly certificate, for "superior trigger avoidance abilities" or something comparable. The picture on the next page presents an overview of trigger management options: (1) Stay away/avoid or (2) Deal with the trigger. Give into the trigger (3) is considered unhealthy! When ready, move onto the next page. Clients will find a list of healthy and unhealthy urge management strategies. The clients should review the list and determine which of the options are UNHEALTHY. Devote the tail end of your session to the reflection questions on the last page: The "Survive a Trigger Planner." Each client should write their own plan. An example is provided.

DAY 11. COPING SKILLS, PAGE 59. *Coping skills* (Roos et al, 2016). This worksheet introduces coping skills, alternatively called "survival strategies," "Life 101," or "Jeez Louise, I'll get through this!" Coping skills are good for handling cravings and triggers and stress, as well as anything life throws at you. As an aside, Days 12-19 introduce many skills, like mindfulness, journaling, and managing feelings, thoughts, and behaviors… and further down the road we visit relationship skills. For now, we present the concept of coping, as well as identifying positive versus negative survival strategies. Start with a question, "What is a coping skill?" Query reasons one would need such a skill, ask for examples, then pass out the worksheet. Review the tips on the second page, pausing to discuss each item. Questions might include, "Why do we need more than one coping skill?" "Why isn't there a single method that fixes everything? (Could that even exist?)," "And why on Earth would anyone practice unhealthy stress-management?" Page 3 includes a list of good and bad skills; make sure clients fold the paper back to hide the answers before identifying the problematic strategies in the bunch. The final exercise is a word search featuring a short list of must-have skills. Have clients raise their hand if they've tried each strategy, then rate efficacy, asking "How can you make the skill more effective?" Make sure to reserve time for the Reflection questions, where clients apply the information to themselves.

DAY 12. ACCEPTING FEELINGS, PAGE 64. *Writing therapy, narrative therapy, Matrix Model.* Day 12 uses art and narrative therapy to explore emotion. Have clients pick a negative emotion. "Imagine you can see it in front of you. Draw what you imagine." Offer clients colored pencils and markers. Consider adding music. Allow the group about 15 minutes to complete their pic. When finished, add labels. "It's crying like a child," "It's ice-cold to the touch," "It has teeth and smells like oregano." Next, the group should suspend disbelief and imagine having a conversation with the feeling. What does the feeling say? How does the client respond? Make sure these questions are answered in writing. For those who finish too quickly, have them draw and engage with a second emotion. Use the rest of the session to discuss the experience, and promote conversation using the reflection questions.

DAY 13. MINDFULNESS, PAGE 66. *Mindfulness* (Sancho et al, 2018; Schumer et al, 2018; O'Leary et al, 2015). Mindfulness soothes pain. It's an anchor during difficult moments, amplifies positive experiences, and ties us into the present. It can be beneficial no matter how one feels, good or bad. Go over the instructions, then use the rest of the session to practice mindful listening. As an experiment, have clients fill out the exercise twice, first listening to pre-recorded sounds (forest or city noises, a piano symphony, etc.) and then to the noises in the room. Compare each experience. If patients wish to share, even better! Don't judge their efforts. Rather, discuss ways to better incorporate mindfulness into their lives: Why, how, and when?

DAY 14. GRATITUDE, PAGE 70. *Gratitude* (O'Leary et al, 2015; Krentzman, 2020). This worksheet is about thankfulness. Ask the group, "Why be thankful for anything? Seriously, does gratitude make a difference? How? How often should you consciously appreciate the good stuff? Oh, and is there anyone who has nothing to be thankful for? Really?" That said, pass out the worksheet, reviewing the instructions before hitting the second page. Encourage clients to dig deep, and once they finish their preliminary thoughts, use the bulleted questions on the third page to broaden their list. They should fill the page until it's overflowing! If you have time left over, give clients the option to color the illustration or perform the more academic task of finding words in the expression GRATITUDE LIST. Give them extra credit for excluding all sexual innuendos.

DAY 15. JOURNALING, PAGE 73. *Journaling* (Krentzman, 2020). Ready for journaling? The exercise will be old hat for some. Others will groan at the thought. To improve the situation, do your best to create a mood, whether it be fancy pens, music, incense, or popcorn, and tell clients today is a day of writing. Consider handing out samples of other people's diary entries. Think Leonardo da Vinci's notebook, Charles Darwin, Courtney Love, and a child's diary. Something funny or earth-shattering even better! Next, review pages 1-2 then have clients jump in pen first. They should write and write and finish pages 3-4 from start to end. Have additional writing prompts available for anyone who needs them. Examples might include writing about feelings, a fun or funny experience, an interesting TV show, or the people most admired in their lives. Individuals might or might not want to share. Finally, spend a few minutes discussing what the writing experience was like. If you're up for more reading, give them homework to do another diary entry. It's a great way to learn about your clients and a superb coping skill you've got them practicing... a win-win situation.

DAY 16. RECOGNIZING PROBLEM THOUGHTS, PAGE 79. *Cognitive behavioral therapy* (Beck et al, 1993; McHugh et al, 2010), *Matrix Model.* Ah, problem thoughts. They ruin your day, wreak havoc on mood, and give you urges to do bad things! But how to introduce the notion of a problem thought? One idea is to present half a dozen pictures, each featuring an emotionally painful situation... for example, an anxious woman trying to sing in front of a crowd, a man stuck in prison, or an exhausted youth facing a huge tower of books he needs to study. (Collect images by looking for clip art online). Ask questions about each image, "What is the character thinking? How does that thought make them feel? How does it make them act? Is this a type of thought you'd like to have?" Point out the "problem thoughts." Next, review the first two pages of the worksheet, using the quiz to differentiate between healthy and unhealthy thoughts. When ready, go to the third page. Here each client must choose a major task or situation in their life and record all doubts in the box provided. It's not time to rewrite, just recognize. Ask each person, "How does the thought make you feel?" "What does it make you want to do?" "Is it a problem thought? Why or why not?" Use the reflection questions to bring the session to an end.

DAY 17. CHANGING PROBLEM THOUGHTS, PAGE 82. *Cognitive behavioral therapy, Matrix Model.* This is the second of two CBT worksheets. First, we revisit problem thought recognition in a little more detail, then jump into managing them. First, clients describe a major task or situation, plus their doubts about the situation. Each individual should choose a specific thought they'd like to improve. Remember, automatic negative thoughts must be specific. "My boss was nasty to me today, so I'm useless" is better than "I'm a failure." Next, introduce the scenario... WORRY and WISDOM. Explain that WORRY is that awkward, insecure part of you that believes the painful thought. Elicit examples, statements like "I can't do this task, I fail at everything" or "Dad thinks I'm using, so I should go ahead and use." WISDOM is the infinitely insightful, informed, laid back, and humored part of your personality that corrects misinterpretations; it raises self-esteem and promotes recovery. A conversation starts between WORRY and WISDOM. What is said? Clients should follow the prompts in the boxes to explore each character's point of view. WORRY is allowed a chance to complain. WISDOM listens carefully, examines the facts, and reaches a healthier conclusion. This is no easy task. You might need to assist with the rewrites, especially if this is the group's first exposure to CBT. Also, check in with everyone once they finish: Sometimes a client will complain that WISDOM has spoken and, still, they feel no better. If this is the case, it's possible the individual doesn't believe what they've written. Remind them the new thought must be believable. How can they adjust it so it's credible? This takes practice. Congratulate their efforts, not the content.

DAY 18. REPLACING DRUGS WITH THE GOOD STUFF, PAGE 87 *Change* (DiClemente, 2018). Without drugs, clients will often complain of giant holes in their lives. It's a vacuum and can easily lead to trouble. It's important to fill that hole with the "good stuff." At this level, we introduce fun. After going through the little exercise at the front, the worksheet introduces a "fun list." It's goofy but worth a look-over. When ready, remind them there's so much more than fun. "Are there other activities we can do to replace drugs? Ones that aren't fun?" Ohh, the list is a long one. What about activities that give you a sense of achievement? What about ones that promote health, friendship, growth, reflection, spirituality, goals and hobbies, and purpose? Education, employment, cat-rearing, professional sports? Sometimes these goals can feel overwhelming and impossible. Remind them to take it slow. Anything is possible. It just takes time. The day ends with a code for solving, a very serious quotation by Nelson Mandela.

DAY 19. NEEDS AND WANTS: MAKING A SCHEDULE, PAGE 90. *Matrix Model.* Planning the day is an essential skill for people in early recovery, one they often haven't mastered. Day 19 takes on schedule-building. The worksheet is deceptively long, but the first four pages can be completed in 20 minutes. They involve a quiz and some helpful hints; most importantly, they introduce the idea of "wants" versus "needs." *Wants* are fun things. *Needs* are behaviors that give you a sense of achievement. Have clients give examples of each before moving on. Page 5 and 6 are reserved for actual schedule-building. Before having clients write their own schedule, consider presenting a sample, keeping it short and interesting. It's best to read and show it in written form, if possible.

> "My to-do list includes (1) getting to my job on-time (where I invent life-saving hats and get rid of all poverty), (2) feeding my pet snake Gerkin, (3) trying out a new roller coaster ride in California, (4) studying Zulu, (5) cuddling with my parrot, (6) buying a new car, and (7) taking my weekly bath."

Ask, "Which are needs? Which are wants? There's no time to do it all, so which tasks are most important? Which should I choose for my schedule?" Point out that the job sounds important, whereas the roller coaster probably not so much. As a group, pull together a quick, fake schedule. Now it's their turn. Using this process, clients should write their own schedule. First, they write their to-do lists. Check for both WANTS and NEEDS. The second step, prioritization, can be especially challenging. If needed, have clients put their to-do list in order, from most to least important. Next, they write the schedule itself. The Reflection on the final page touches on an important task, how to incorporate the schedule into their lives.

DAY 20. HONESTY, PAGE 98. *Matrix Model, social skills* (Ersogutcu et al, 2016; O'Leary et al, 1976; Platt, 1993; Platt et al, 1989; Ramezani et al, 2012; Stevens et al, 2015). Day 20 is about earning back trust – if or when possible. Talking about honesty is an enormous conversation, so best take your time. Consider dividing the exercise into two sessions. As a start, we recommend 15-20 minutes of conversation before passing out the worksheet.

Ask clients about their experience with trust since quitting: Did family and old friends suddenly trust them? Some will say they're not trusted at all and express frustration over this. Challenge the group with the quotation found at the beginning of the worksheet. Can trust be earned back at all? Ask if anyone has successfully earned back trust – if so, how did they do it? If not… really, no one? That's telling. What, do drugs and alcohol make a person untrustworthy? What do the group think? Answers might surprise you. Don't give an opinion yourself, just allow the conversation to unfold. Finally, ask clients to come up with "methods" to earn back trust. Brainstorm as many approaches as you can. That said, introduce the idea that life is more complicated than a list – but a list is a good start.

When ready, jump into the "Trusting a lawyer" quiz. Use the scenario to continue conversation and examine misconceptions. In the end, yes, trust can sometimes be earned back, but that happens little by little and over a long period of time. Expecting things to be faster isn't realistic. The Reflection on the final page invites clients to write a letter to their loved ones describing three things they plan to do to be more trustworthy.

DAY 21. BEING A GOOD FRIEND, PAGE 102. *Matrix Model, social skills.* This worksheet is the first in a sequence about friendship skills. Addiction can wreak havoc on relationships, and part of the remedy is learning how to be a better friend. If you're working with a group, we recommend NOT sharing this handout, as they'll read ahead and voilá, you've lost them. Rather, review pages 1-3 slowly, reading each box two or three times. Keep in mind the boxes shouldn't be read in numeric order. #1 takes you to #4, which takes you to #7. Follow the prompts for each situation, discussing the skill, and use the associated questions to drive discussion. Skills include listening, empathy, respect, and keeping promises, but don't stop there. Ask about other characteristics that make for a good friend. Jot down clients' ideas in a visible place, *then* pass out the worksheet. The first three pages have already been reviewed. The crossword puzzle on page 4 lists characteristics of good friendships; give the group time to unscramble each word and plug them into the crossword puzzle, then discuss each one. As usual, ask questions, "Has anyone ever had a friendship where the other person had no time for you? What was that like?" "What does it mean to be available?" "Why is patience important?"

DAY 22. ASSERTIVE COMMUNICATION, PAGE 106. *Social skills.* Assertive communication is an important skill many of our clients don't understand. Often, they mistaken assertive communication with standing up for one's own rights, aggression even. Emphasize this isn't quite right, but don't provide a definition just yet. This worksheet is divided into two parts. Part 1 (pages 1-2) helps individuals identify their own communication style. Read the questions and have each person circle their answer. When finished, pass out pages 3 and help clients choose their corresponding style. Discuss all three styles. The healthiest type of communication is Option B. *Note this quiz isn't an official communication inventory but rather a humble, informal, and quick introduction.* The last two pages of the worksheet introduce the characteristics of assertive communication. Client get to "practice" by solving fake scenarios. Here are some sample answers:

"I think you're hungry and need more food, thus stealing my tomatoes. If you stop stealing them, I'll give you a hot meal once a day."

"Honey, I understand you wanted a motorcycle too. If you can wait a couple months, we'll save up enough money to buy you that bad-ass bike you like."

"I think you're saying that you like playing drums late because you don't have time during the day. However, it seems you have time in the evenings? I request that you not play after midnight because I can't sleep and I'm doing poorly at work.

Note that assertiveness skills are divided into easier pointers on page 4 and more advanced on page 5. If your group is up for it, approach the final page and ask questions as you go: "How do 'I' statements make things better?" "Should you consider the needs of the other person if they're in the wrong? Yes, but why?" "If the other person's needs are greater than yours, should you always give in?" Finally, in the Reflection, clients are encouraged to apply these skills to a personal situation.

DAY 23. GOOD VS. BAD RELATIONSHIPS, PAGE 111. *Matrix Model, social skills.* Sometimes we engage in toxic relationships without knowing it, or we're aware but don't know what to do. This worksheet takes on these two tasks: (1) identifying unhealthy connections and (2) dealing with these connections when they can't be avoided. We start by presenting a scenario and set of questions to explore healthy versus unhealthy relationships. Review the answers in depth and have clients create a list of characteristics of both types of relationships. The cartoon on page 2 helps clarify these characteristics. Next, clients are encouraged to examine their own relationships and divide them into healthy, in-between, and toxic. Ask the group how they deal with bad relationships, then turn to the final page for more ideas. The Reflection questions at the bottom personalize the worksheet; clients must decide how to deal with a tough relationship in their lives. *Note, if anyone is dealing with abuse, get them a list of crisis numbers, emphasizing they should hide it well and reach out when *they* are ready. *If there are children involved, you're required to report it to the authorities.**

DAY 24. THE ASTOUNDING WORLD, PAGE 116. *Self-esteem, positive psychology* (Hoeppner et al, 2018; Krentzman, 2013). In a couple words, this worksheet promotes love for life. An interesting way to start the session is with a little confession: "I'm going to show you some of the greatest things I've seen. You're not allowed to share this with anyone, ha ha!" Then show them 10-15 pictures of what has made your life worthwhile – not too elaborate, nothing extremely personal. Ideas might include your pet iguana, Star Wars, a sunset, people swimming with a dolphin, or you with a funny haircut. If you're in a goofy mood, add an outlier: someone climbing a building, punctuated with, "Naw, just kidding." Once you've shared your fill, share this worksheet. The theme is "I've seen great things you wouldn't believe." Clients should spend most of the class completing the sentences. If you're up to it, let the group use magazine clippings, poetry, music lyrics, and artwork too. If a client can't come up with any ideas, they should write about what they want to see. Worst-case scenario, hand out magazines and ask for pictures instead of words.

DAY 25. A WELL-LIVED LIFE, PAGE 119. *Writing therapy, self-esteem, positive psychology.* We all need something to look forward to. In treatment for substance use disorders, we often focus so much on the immediate… avoiding cravings, learning coping skills, rewriting thoughts… that the future exists as a giant, gray question-mark. For clients, that can be terrifying. This final worksheet introduces the future as an exciting place. The whole purpose is to appeal to that part of us that needs to believe everything can turn out okay. It isn't logical. There are no promises. But creating a positive version of your future establishes a template for action, a direction to walk---and clients need this. Encourage your patients to write, then write some more. Back that up with uplifting music and incense, and draw out the experience as much as possible. Later, to expand their future further, they can focus on the questions on the second page. Every detail counts. In the end, if patients share their work with you, ponder and think: that's their future in your hands, what a gift! End the session with the Reflection questions.

FINALE: WHEN YOU FINISH THIS BOOK. This worksheet is a bonus round. After a quick review of the workbook's contents, it divides into two tasks. One is a spin-off of a worksheet from the Original Outside-the-Box Recovery Workbook, "The New You in Recovery" – given all their effort and the positive things they've embraced, the client introduces their sober new identity. The other task identifies what activities they've chosen to replace drugs.

BONUS WORKSHEETS.

COPING SKILLS: THE "DID IT WORK?" CARD. *Coping skills.* There are dozens of coping skills in this workbook. This card is a useful way to gauge whether clients are using them and the skill's level of efficacy.

RESOURCES FOR YOUR JOURNEY. MOTIVATION: DO YOU WANT TO QUIT? *Motivational Interviewing* (Miller et al, 2012). This worksheet is a good place to start if clients are at a contemplative stage of recovery or new to drug treatment.

APPENDIX C. REFERENCES

- Alcohol & Drug Self-Help Network, Inc (2013). *Smart Recovery Handbook: Tools and Strategies to Help You on Your Recovery Journey.* Mentor, OH: Smart Recovery.
- Aletraris L, Paino M, Edmond M, Roman P, Bride B (2014). The use of art and music therapy in substance abuse treatment programs. *Journal of Addictions Nursing* 25(4): 190-196.
- Bhattacharjee D, Rai A, Singh N, Kumar P, Munda S, Das B (2011). Psychoeducation: A measure to strengthen psychiatric treatment. *Delhi Psychiatry Journal* 14(1): 33-39
- Beaufort F (2017). *Recovery Through Creativity: Overcoming Superhero Syndrome.* Bloomington, IN: Balboa Press.
- Beck A, Newman C, Wright F, et al (1993). *Cognitive Therapy of Substance Abuse.* New York, NY: Guilford Press
- Bolton G, Howlett S, Lago C, Wright J (2004). *Writing Cures: An Introductory Handbook of Writing in Counseling and Therapy.* Abingdon, Oxon (England): Routledge Publishers.
- Courbasson C, Endler N, Kocovski L (2002). Coping and psychological distress for men with substance use disorders. *Current Psychiatry* 21.
- Diamond J (2002). *Narrative Means to Sober Ends: Treating Addiction and its Aftermath.* New York/London: Guilford Press.
- DiClemente C (2018). *Addiction and Change: How Addiction Develops and Addicted People Recover,* 2nd Edition. New York, NY: Guilford Substance Abuse.
- Dingle G, Williams E, Jetten J, Welch J (2017). Choir singing and creative writing enhance emotion regulation in adults with chronic mental health conditions. *British Journal of Clinical Psychology* 56: 4.
- Ersogutcu F, Karakas S (2016). Social functioning and self-esteem of substance abuse patients. *Archives of Psychiatric Nursing* 30(5): 587-592
- Eschleman K, Madsen J, Alarcon G, Barelka A (2014). Benefiting from creative activity: The positive relationships between creative activity, recovery experiences, and performance-related outcomes. *Journal of Occupational and Organizational Psychology* 87(3): 579-598.
- Gardner P, Poole J (2009). One story at a time: Narrative therapy, older adults, and addictions. *Journal of Applied Gerontology* 28(5): 600-620.
- Garte-Wolf S(2011). Narrative therapy group work for chemically dependent clients with HIV/AIDS. *Social Work with Groups* 34: 330-338.
- Hendershot C, Witkiewitz K, George W, Marlatt GA (2011). Relapse prevention for addictive behaviors. *Substance Abuse Treatment, Prevention, and Policy* 6:17.
- Hoeppner B, Schick M, Carlon H, Hoeppner S (2018). Do self-administered positive psychology exercises work in persons in recovery from problematic substance use? An online randomized survey. *Journal of Substance Abuse Treatment* 99: 16-23.
- Kavanagh D, Andrade J, May J (2004). Beating the urge: Implications of research into substance-related desires. *Addictive Behaviors* 29(7): 1359-1372
- Kougiali Z, Fasulo A, Needs A, et al (2017). Planting seeds of change: Directionality in the narrative construction of recovery from addiction. *Psychology & Health* 32(6): 639-288.

- Krentzman A (2020). How a gratitude and positive activity journal supports recovery from alcohol and other substance use disorders: a framework derived from grounded theory. Retrieved from the *University of Minnesota Digital Conservancy.*
- Krentzman, A (2013). Review of the application of positive psychology to substance use, addiction, and recovery research. *Psychology of Addictive Behaviors 27*(1): 151-165.
- Kreuter, E (2020). Incorporation of expressive writing in the treatment of drug and alcohol addiction. *Journal of Poetry Therapy* 33(3): 179-186
- Matto H (2002). Integrating art therapy methodology in brief inpatient substance abuse treatment in adults. *Journal of Social Work Practice in the Addictions* 2(2): 69-83.
- Matto H, Corcoran J, Fassler A (2003). Integrating solution-focused and art therapies for substance abuse treatment: Guidelines for practice. *The Arts in Psychotherapy* 30: 265-272.
- McHugh RK, Hearon B, Otto M (2010), Cognitive Behavioral Therapy for substance use disorders. *Psychiatric Clinic North America* 33(3): 511-525
- McConnell D, Snoek A (2018). The importance of self-narration in recovery from addiction. *Philosophy, Psychiatry, and Psychology* 25(3): E31-E44.
- McKay, J (2016). Making the hard work of recovery more attractive for those with substance use disorders. *Addiction Debate* 112(5).
- Miller W, Rollnick S (2012). *Motivational Interviewing: Helping People Change,* 3rd Edition. New York, NY: Guildford Press
- O'Leary D, O'Leary M (1976): Social skill acquisition and psychosocial development of alcoholics: A review. *Addictive Behaviors* 1(2): 111-120
- O'Leary K, Dockray S (2015). The effects of two novel gratitude and mindfulness interventions on Well-Being. *The Journey of Alternative and Complementary Medicine* 21(4)
- Pinhasi-Vittorio (2018). Writing, sharing, and healing: The interplay of literacy in the healing journey of the recovering from substance abuse. *Journal of Poetry Therapy* 31(4): 209-223
- Platt J, Hermalin J (1993). An overview of problem-solving and social skills approaches in substance abuse treatment. *Psychotherapy: Theory, Research, Practice, Training* 30(2): 276-283
- Platt JJ, Hermalin J (1989). Social skills deficit interventions for substance abusers. *Psychology of Addictive Behaviors* 3(3): 114-133.
- Ramezani H, Rafie H, Khodaie M, et al (2012). Determining the efficacy of social skills training in treatment of drug addiction in patients referring to Tehran Clinic. *Scientific Journal of Rehabilitative Medicine* 1(1): 63-72
- Rawson R, Obert J, McCann M, Ling W (2005). *The Matrix Model Intensive Outpatient Alcohol and Drug Treatment Program.* Center City, MN: Hazelden Information and Educational Services
- Richter S, Brown S, Mott M (1991). The impact of social support and self-esteem on adolescent substance abuse treatment outcome. *Journal of Substance Abuse* 3(4): 371-385
- Robins R, Trzesniewski K, Donnellan MB (2012). A Brief Primer on Self-Esteem. *The Prevention Researcher* 19 (2)
- Roos C, Witkiewitz K (2016). Adding tools to the toolbox: The role of coping repertoire in alcohol treatment. *Journal of Consulting and Clinical Psychology* 84(7): 599-611
- Sancho M, De Gracia M, Rodriquez R, et al (2018): Mindfulness-based interventions for the treatment of substance and behavioral addictions. *Frontier Psychiatry* 29

- Schumer M, Lindsay E, Creswell J (2018). Brief mindfulness training for negative affectivity. *Journal of Consulting and Clinical Psychology* 86(7): 569-583
- Sharp M (2018). Art therapy and the recovery process: A literature review. *Expressive Therapies Capstone Theses* 30.
- Snead B, Pakstis D, Evans B, Nelson R (2015). The use of creative writing interventions in substance abuse treatment. *Therapeutic Recreation Journal* 49(2): 179-182.
- Stevens E, Jason L, Ram D, Light J (2015). Investigating social support and network relationships in substance use disorder recovery. *Substance Abuse* 36(4): 396-399.
- Springer W (2006). Poetry in therapy: A way to heal for trauma survivors and clients in recovery from addiction, *Journal of Poetry Therapy* 19(2): 69-81
- Swain N, Gibb S, Horwood J, et al (2012). Alcohol and cannabis abuse/dependence symptoms and life satisfaction in young adulthood. *Drug & Alcohol Review* 31(3): 327-333
- Williamson C, Wright J (2018). How creative does writing have to be to be therapeutic? A dialogue on the practice and research of writing to recovery and survive. *Journal of Poetry Therapy* 31(2): 113-123.
- Wilson M (2012). Art therapy in addictions treatment: Creativity and shame reduction. In C. Malchiodi, *Handbook of Art Therapy* (pp. 302-319). New York, NY: Guilford Press.
- Witkiewitz K, Marlatt GA (2007). Overview of relapse prevention. In Witkiewitz K, *Evidence-Based Relapse Prevention* (pp3-18). Burlington, VA: Academic Press.
- Zullig K, Valois R, Huebner ES, et al (2001). Relationship between perceived life satisfaction and adolescents' substance abuse. *Journal of Adolescent Health* 19(4): 279-288

ABOUT DR. KIM & OTB RECOVERY

When not writing strange worksheets, Kim Rosenthal practices life as a psychiatrist caring for residents in a long-term psychiatric hospital in North Carolina. She is known for her arm-flailing, humored "live life!" lectures and often has fireside chats with her patients, topics ranging from understanding friendship to future inventions to exploring caves in Vietnam.

The author has spent most of her career as a travelling doctor. She holds medical licenses in North Carolina, Maine, and Hawaii, and has cared for 10,000+ patients over the years in many settings—hospitals, clinics, detox centers, residential rehabs, ACT teams, emergency rooms, forensic settings, nursing homes, as well as serving our veterans.

Dr. Kim believes that a psychiatrist's role is to support her patients through life's darker moments. Psychiatry is, after all, the art of alleviating suffering. But it is in knowing that each person is unique, that our patient's minds can't simply be stuffed into the diagnostic boxes in our textbooks, where the real work begins: The good clinician takes off her jacket, sits down, listens to what the client has to say, and seeks to hear of their passions and strengths as much as their struggles. They seek joy amidst the shadows.

Rosenthal's *Outside-the-Box Recovery* movement emerged out of necessity. Recovery is tough. Treatment can be so dry and humorless. The fact is people are more likely to pursue and stick with treatment if there's an element of joy and creativity in the process. The purpose of *OTB Recovery* is to promote a passion for sober living through art therapy, writing, puzzles, humor, and other *clinically-relevant* recovery materials. We're also running for US President, but it's too early to talk about that.

OTHER BOOKS BY DR. KIM ROSENTHAL

(original)

THE OUTSIDE-THE-BOX RECOVERY WORKBOOK

GREAT FOR COUNSELORS AND THEIR CLIENTS!

Illustrated, humored, and clinically relevant, the workbook takes the reader on a 30-day introductory journey into the world of sobriety. Available on Amazon.

OUTSIDE-THE-BOX RECOVERY STEP ONE

Balancing serious self-reflection with a flare of the unusual, this little workbook uses illustrations, art therapy, cartoons, layers of questions, and the occasional joke to explore important Step One concepts.
Available on Amazon.

LOOKING FOR MORE RECOVERY MATERIAL? Recovery plan, autopsy of a relapse, CBT, recovery-promotion, quizzes, coloring, and puzzles? Visit *kimrosenthalmd.com* to find lots of free and low-cost material. You can also sign up to get a complimentary copy of the STEP ONE booklet. See you there!

Made in United States
Troutdale, OR
01/22/2024

17064172R00100